ILLUSTRATED ENCYCLOPEDIA

TRACTORS
OF THE WORLD

ILLUSTRATED ENCYCLOPEDIA

TRACTORS
OF THE WORLD

JOHN CARROLL

HERMES
HOUSE

ACKNOWLEDGEMENTS

The publishers would like to thank the following picture libraries and photographers for the use of their pictures in this book:

Agripicture: 37tl; 52br; 61tl (Peter Dean); 72t (Peter Dean).
Alpha Stock: 37r.
John Bolt: 7 (all); 10tr; 11tm, tr, br; 16br; 17tr, b; 21bl, br; 23tl, tr, br; 24t, tr, b; 29t; 38b, tr; 40m, br, bl; 41bl; 46br; 49bl; 50t, bl, br; 53tr, br; 54mr, bl; 58b; 63bl; 68tl, tr; 69br, tr; 73t; 84m; 86bl; 98t, m, b; 100b; 101bl, br; 106tl; 112t, m, b; 121tl, tr, m, b; 128t, m, b; 129tl; 131tl, tr; 132t; 152br; 153tm, tr, b; 155bl.
John Carroll: 16t, bl; 26tr; 27t, b; 29m, b; 34b; 36t, bl, br; 37bl; 38tr; 39bl; 40tr, 41tr; 53tl; 55tl; 58m; 59b; 61tr; 62t, m; 69m; 70tl; 86br; 87t; 99t, m, b; 103bl; 106tr; 114t; 115tl, tr,

b; 116t,; 117t, m, b; 132b; 133br; 135b; 138t, b; 139t, b; 141m; 142t; 147t; 152t.
CDC: 35t.
C.F.C.L.: 41tl; 141b; 146t; Ian Clegg: 39t, mr; 46bl; 48t; 49t, br; 52bl; 61b; 101t, m; 103t, bl; 133bl. **Image Bank:** 144bl (Guido A. Rossi).
Impact: 42m (Tony Page); 70tr (Julian Calder); 144tl (Alain le Garsmeur), ml (Mark Henley), br (Michael Good); 146b (Anne-Marie Purkiss).
Andrew Morland/New Holland/Agco: 1m; 2; 3m; 5m; 8bl, tr, br; 9t, b; 12tl; 14bl, tr; 15tr, m, br; 18t, br; 19; 25t, m, b; 26bl, br; 32; 33b; 35b; 44t; 45br; 46t; 47tl; 52t; 54t, ml; 55tr, br; 56t, m, b; 57tl, tr, bl, br; 59tr; 62b; 63t, br; 65t, m, bl, br; 73b; 94t, m, b; 95t, b; 96t; 106br; 107m, b; 110t, b: 111m, b; 113t, b; 114b; 118t; 119t; 120t; 122t, m, b; 123t, b; 124; 125t, m; 126t, b; 127tl, tr,

b; 129tr, b; 135t; 136; 137bl, br; 140tr, tl, bl, br; 142m, bl, br; 143t, b; 145t, bl, br; 147b; 148t, b; 250bl, br; 251t, b; 154t; 158mr.
Royal Geographical Society. 45t;
Spectrum Colour Library: 28b (E Chalker); t; 34t; 43t; 51t; 59tl; 60t; 72b; 83t; 87b; 88t; 104t; 105b; 106bl; 107t; 116b; 125b; 133t; 155mr; 158tl, b; 159tl, tr.
Still Pictures: 84b (Allan Morgan); 102t (Paul Harrison); 103br (Chris Caldicott); 141t (Pierre Gleizes).
Tony Stone Images: 6 (Art Wolfe); 33t (Billy Nustace); 51b (Bertrand Rieger); 58t; 70bl (John & Eliza Forder); 71tl; 89t; 149t (Arnulf Husmo); 155br (Andrew Sacks); 157b (Andy Sacks); 159b (Bruce Hands).
Gary Stuart: 10bl; 12m, b; 103t, b; 110b, t; 111t; 112tl, m,

br, bl; 30tl, t, b; 31t, b; 42t, b; 43ml, mr, b; 44b; 45bl; 47b; 48b; 53bl; 60tl; 64t, b; 66bl, br; 67t, ml, m, mr, b; 68bl; 69tl; 70m; 71tr, mr, b; 74t, m, b; 75t, m, b; 76t, ml, mr, b; 77m, b; 78t, bl, br; 79t, m, b; 80t, m, b; 81t, m, b; 82tr, m, tl, b; 83b; 84t; 85t, m, b; 86t; 87m; 88m, b; 89bl, br; 90t, b; 91t, m, b; 92t, b; 93t, m, b; 96 b; 97t, m, b; 100t; 102m, b; 103m; 104b; 105t, ml, mr; 108t, m, b; 109tr, tl, ml, b; 111t; 119b; 120b; 130t, m, b; 131b; 134; 149b; 150t; 153bl,; 154m, b; 155t; 156t, b; 157t, m; 159m.
Superstock: 55br; 66t; 69bl; 77t; 118b.

t=top b=bottom l=left r=right m=middle tr= top right tl=top left ml=middle left mr=middle right bl=bottom left br=bottom right lm=left middle

This edition published by Hermes House an imprint of Anness Publishing Limited Hermes House, 88-89 Blackfriars Road, London SE1 8HA

© Anness Publishing Limited 2000

A CIP catalogue record for this book is available from the British Library

Publisher Joanna Lorenz
Project Editor Helen Marsh
Designer Michael Morey
Picture Researcher John Bolt
Reader Kate Henderson
Production Controller Don Campaniello

Previously published as part of a larger compendium,
The World Encyclopedia of Tractors and Farm Machinery

1 3 5 7 9 10 8 6 4 2

Contents

INTRODUCTION

Here follows a list of the major tractor manufacturers and their most important machines, stretching back to the beginning of the 20th century. The A-Z also illustrates how, throughout its history, the tractor manufacturing industry has been characterized by numerous mergers and amalgamations. Where once there were hundreds of minor manufacturers producing small numbers of farm machines, there is now just a handful of multinational corporations making thousands of tractors. Also apparent is how quickly innovations in tractor manufacture spread. For example, Henry Ford offered the new and innovative Fordson in 1917; within a few years his style of tractor had become the norm and the basic configuration of the Fordson is still followed by manufacturers today. Computers and global positioning systems are the latest technologies to be applied to the farm tractor, and undeniably have a place in today's modern agriculture.

■ OPPOSITE *Technology supersedes tradition in Tian Shan Province, China.*

■ LEFT *A gleaming 1951 David Brown Cropmaster.*

AGCO ALLIS

During the mid-1980s the well-known Allis-Chalmers tractor brand became Deutz-Allis under the ownership of Klockner-Humboldt-Deutz, based in the German city of Cologne. In 1990 the Deutz-Allis division was sold to the Allis-Gleaner Company (AGCO), which later reintroduced the brand as AGCO Allis tractors. These machines are produced as one of its numerous brands of AGCO farming equipment. The relatively recently established range of AGCO Allis tractors incorporates several different series, including those that are designated as 5600, 6670, 8700 and 9700 models.

The 5600 Series models are mid-sized machines and range from the 45hp 5650 to the 63hp 5670. They are powered by direct injection air-cooled diesel engines. The 5600 models are designed to be capable of tight turns and to drive a wide variety of equipment from the power take-off (PTO). The given horsepower figures are measured at the PTO. The AGCO Allis 6670

■ RIGHT *The Model 9690 is a two-wheel-drive AGCO Allis tractor manufactured in 1996. Seen here with twin rear wheels, it is one of the company's largest tractors.*

tractor is a row crop tractor that produces 63 PTOhp; it is powered by a four-cylinder direct injection air-cooled diesel engine. Reactive hydrostatic power steering is designed to end drift and what is termed the "economical PTO" setting is designed to save fuel by

reducing engine speed by 25 per cent on jobs that do not require full PTO power.

The 8745 and 8765 Models are large capacity AGCO Allis tractors designed for large-scale farming. The 8765 is available with a choice of all-wheel drive or two-wheel drive and produces

■ ABOVE *The AGCO Allis 6690 model is one of the company's 6600 Series and is powered by an air-cooled diesel engine.*

■ LEFT *The 6690 is a four-wheel-drive AGCO Allis tractor. This is a 1994 example that uses different diameter front and rear wheels.*

■ LEFT *Note the modern stylized curved hood on this four-wheel-drive 1995 AGCO Allis 9435 model.*

85hp at the PTO while the 8745 produces 70 PTOhp. Both come with 12-speed synchronized shuttle transmissions which are designed to offer sufficient power in all gears. These tractors have an AGCO Allis 400 Series turbocharged diesel engine providing the power under the bodywork, which is of a modern "low-profile" appearance. The larger tractors in the 8700 Series are the 8775 and 8785 Models, powered by a fuel-efficient AGCO Allis 600 Series liquid-cooled diesel. These tractors produce 95hp and 110hp at the PTO respectively. They are manufactured with a choice of all-wheel drive and two-wheel-drive transmissions. The transmission has four forward speeds and an optional creeper gear. The tractors are also equipped with a 540/1000 "economy PTO", a durable wet multi-disc clutch and electronically

controlled three-point hitch. The 125 PTOhp 9735 and 145 PTOhp 9745 Models are tractors that have been designed with styling and performance in mind. Both are available in an all-wheel-drive version or as a standard model with either four- or 18-speed transmissions.

The two turbocharged 9600 Series models are fitted with a liquid-cooled engine of up to 8700cc/530cu in displacement. The 175 PTOhp 9675 and the 195 PTOhp 9695 tractors feature Powershift electronic transmission and a cab-forward design.

New advanced computer technology has recently been employed in the manufacture of the AGCO Allis range. The proprietary system known as DataTouch is designed to be a compact, easy-to-read, touch-screen display, from which all the functions of the in-cab systems can be controlled. The system has been designed so that there are no cables in the operator's line of sight. The system is based on simple touch-screen technology that is considered by the manufacturer to be easy to use despite the complexity of the operations and data it controls.

ALLIS - CHALMERS

■ BELOW *From 1929 onwards Allis-
Chalmers tractors were painted in a bright
shade of orange. It was known as Persian
Orange and was an attempt to attract
new customers.*

This tractor maker has roots that stretch
back to Milwaukee's Reliance Works
Flour Milling Company that was
founded in 1847. The company was
reorganized in 1912 with Brigadier
General Otto H. Falk as president. It
remained based in Milwaukee,
Wisconsin and, although it had no
experience of steam traction, built its
first gasoline tractor, the tricycle-type
Model 10–18, in 1914. This had a two-
cylinder opposed engine that revved to
720rpm and, as its designation
indicates, produced 10 drawbar hp and
18 belt hp. It was started on gasoline but
once the engine warmed up it ran on
cheaper kerosene. The single wheel was
at the front while the driver sat over the
rear axle.

Unlike some of its competitors, Allis-
Chalmers did not have an established
dealer network around the United States
so sales did not achieve their full
potential. Between 1914 and 1921 the
company manufactured and sold
approximately, 2,700 10–18s. Some of

■ BELOW *The Allis-Chalmers Model B tractor
was exported from the United States to Britain
under the Lend-Lease policies of the war.*

these were sold through mail order
catalogues, and during World War I
some export sales were achieved. The
French imported American tractors and
sold them under their own brand names
– the Allis-Chalmers 10–18, for
instance, was marketed in France as the
Globe tractor.

The conventional Model 18–30
tractor, introduced in 1919, was
powered by a vertical in-line four-
cylinder engine. In the early days sales
were limited, partially as a result of
competition from the cheap Fordson,
and only slightly more than 1,000 had
been assembled by 1922, but over the
course of the next seven years the total
reached 16,000.

Allis-Chalmers acquired a few other
companies when the end of the post-war
boom led to numerous closures and
mergers within the tractor industry.
Among these acquisitions was the

■ RIGHT *The Allis-Chalmers Model U had a lengthy production run that extended between its introduction in 1929 and end of production in 1953.*

■ BELOW *On top of the orange paint, the A-C logo left no doubt as to which make the operator was driving.*

Monarch Tractor Company of Springfield, Illinois, that made crawler tractors. The company had started tractor production in 1917 and had reorganized twice by the time of the merger, when production of a range of six different-sized crawlers was under way. The smallest of these was the Lightfoot 6–10 and the largest the Monarch 75, which weighed 11.5 tons. Allis-Chalmers continued the production of crawlers in Springfield. Another of its acquisitions was the Advance-Rumely Thresher Company, that was taken over in 1931.

In 1929 as many as 32 companies making farm equipment merged to form the United Tractor and Equipment Corporation, which had its headquarters in Chicago, Illinois. Amongst the 32 was Allis-Chalmers, which was contracted to build a new tractor powered by a Continental engine and known as the United. The tractor was launched at an agricultural show in Wichita in the spring of 1929. The corporation did not stay in business long. Allis-Chalmers was fortunate enough to survive the collapse and continued to build the United tractor, albeit redesignated the Model U. The Model U and E tractors became the basis of the Allis-Chalmers range. Allis-Chalmers also introduced a distinctive colour scheme to attract new customers and differentiate its tractors from those of other makers. The colour chosen was called Persian Orange. It was a simple ploy but one that no doubt worked, as other manufacturers soon followed suit with brightly coloured paintwork and stylized bonnets, radiator grilles and mudguards.

The Model U later became famous as the first tractor available with low-pressure pneumatic rubber tyres. In 1932 Model U tractors fitted with

ALLIS-CHALMERS MODEL U	
Year	1933
Engine	Four cylinder
Power	34hp on kerosene
Transmission	Four speed (pneumatic tyres)
Weight	n/k

■ BELOW *The Allis-Chalmers Model U played an important part in the development of pneumatic tyres for tractors as the company used a number of them to demonstrate Firestone tyres.*

aircraft-type tyres inflated to 15psi were successfully tested on a dairy farm in Waukesha, Wisconsin. Despite their proven ability, pneumatic tyres were greeted with scepticism by those who thought that such tyres would not be adequate for farming use. Allis-Chalmers indulged in a series of speed events involving pneumatic-tyred tractors to promote this latest breakthrough in tractor technology. They went as far as hiring professional racing drivers to demonstrate their pneumatic-tyred machines at agricultural shows and state fairs. In the late 1930s, Allis-Chalmers introduced its Model A and B

■ LEFT *A 1942 version of the long-running Allis-Chalmers Model U which pioneered the use of pneumatic tyres. Steel rims reappeared during World War II as a result of rubber shortages.*

tractors. The four-speed Model A replaced the Model E and was made between 1936 and 1942, while production of the Model B ran between 1937 and 1957. The Model B was powered by a four-cylinder 15.7bhp engine and more than 127,000 were made over the course of the lengthy production run. In 1936 the Model U was upgraded by the fitment of the company's own UM engine. The Model WC was introduced in 1934 as the first tractor designed for pneumatic tyres, although steel rims remained available as an option. In 1938 Allis-Chalmers offered the downsized Model B tractor on pneumatic tyres, a successful sales ploy. The tractor sold particularly well and was widely marketed. It was manufactured in Great Britain after World War II for sale in both the home and export markets. In another move to increase sales in the same year, the company increased the number of its tractor models with styled hoods and radiator grille shells.

Many established American tractor manufacturers quickly added new models to their ranges in the immediate post-war years. Allis-Chalmers introduced its Models G and WD. The Model WD-45 was fitted with a gasoline engine. In 1955 a diesel variant was offered and this marked something of a landmark for Allis-Chalmers as it was

■ BELOW *The three-point linkage, as seen on this WD-45, revolutionized the attachment of farm implements to tractors.*

■ BOTTOM *The Allis-Chalmers WD-45 was one of the first all-new post-World War II tractors.*

the first wheeled diesel tractor the company had launched, though it had been making diesel-engined crawlers since taking over Monarch in the late 1920s. The diesel engine selected for the WD-45 was an in-line six-cylinder of 3770cc/230cu in displacement. An LPG engine option was also made available for the WD-45 and it was the first model Allis-Chalmers offered with power steering. The WD-45 was a great success overall and more than 83,000 were eventually made.

Allis-Chalmers produced the Model B tractor at a plant in Southampton, England, from 1948, although by then it was already considered an old-fashioned tractor. The British plant was moved to Essendine in Lincolnshire soon afterwards and the D270 went into production. This was in some ways an updated Model B, featuring high ground clearance – which made it suitable for use with mid-mounted implements – and a choice of three engines, all from later Model B tractors. These included petrol and paraffin versions of the in-line, four-cylinder, overhead-valve unit and a Perkins P3 diesel. The petrol and

■ LEFT *A restored Allis-Chalmers WD-45, with adjustable rear wheel tread.*

■ BELOW *The Model C was made between 1940 and 1948 and featured a tricycle-type wheel arrangement for row crop use.*

paraffin engines produced 27hp and 22hp at 1650rpm respectively. The D272 was a further upgraded version offered from 1959 and the ED40 was another new model introduced in 1960. Disappointing sales of these models, amongst other factors, caused Allis-Chalmers to stop making tractors in Britain in 1968.

In 1955, the company bought the Gleaner Harvester Corporation and introduced its D Series in the latter part of that decade. This was a comprehensive range of tractors that included numerous D-prefixed models including the D10, D12, D14, D15, D17, D19 and D21 machines. There were up to 50 variations in the series once the various fuel options of gasoline, diesel and LPG were considered. The D17 was powered by a 4293cc/262cu in engine that produced 46 drawbar and 51 belt hp in the Nebraska Tractor Tests. There were 62,540 Model D17s made during the tractor's ten-year production run.

In 1960 the company changed the livery used on its products, selecting an even brighter hue, named Persian Orange Number 2, which was contrasted with cream wheels and radiator grilles. The most important models to benefit from this change were the D10 and D12,

tractors which had superseded the Models B and CA. Their production run lasted ten years but fewer than 10,000 were made.

The last Allis-Chalmers tractors were produced during the mid-1980s because in 1985 the company, hit by the recession, was taken over by a West German company. Klockner-Humboldt-Deutz acquired it and renamed the tractor division Deutz-Allis. It was shortlived: in 1990 the company was

acquired by an American holding firm, known as Allis-Gleaner Company (AGCO), which soon renamed the tractor producer AGCO Allis.

One of the final Allis-Chalmers tractors was the Model 4W-305 of 1985. It had a twin turbo engine that produced power in the region of 305hp and a transmission that included 20 forward gears and four reverse. Production of tractors at West Allis, Wisconsin, ceased in December 1985.

OTHER MAKES

(ACME, Advance-Rumely, American
Harvester, Avance, Belarus, Bolinder
Munktell, Braud, Breda, Brockway, Bull)

■ ACME

ACME was one of a lengthy list of shortlived tractor manufacturers founded during
the boom years that followed the end of
World War I. The ACME tractor was
advertised as being available in both
wheeled and half-track form. It is hard to
say with complete certainty but it is likely
that many small companies which
advertised tractors, such as this one, never
made more than a handful of machines after
their initial prototype. This was one reason
why the Nebraska Tractor Tests, started in
1920, were to become such a useful
consumer aid for farmers.

■ ADVANCE-RUMELY

Meinrad Rumely was a German emigrant
who set up a blacksmith's shop in La Porte,
Indiana during the 1850s. His smithy was
gradually expanded into a factory that built
farm machines and steam engines for
agricultural use. In 1908 John Secor joined
the company to develop an oil-fuelled
engine, and Rumely, which had primarily
been a thresher manufacturer, made its first
OilPull tractor in 1909 after Secor had
perfected a carburettor for kerosene or
paraffin fuel. A later result of this
development work was the Model B 25–45
tractor that in turn was superseded by the

■ LEFT
A 40-60 Advance-
Rumely tractor of
1929. Noted for
the manufacture of
large tractors, the
company was
acquired by Allis-
Chalmers in 1931.

■ BELOW LEFT
Early tractors such
as this Advance-
Rumely took many
of their design
features from the
steam traction
engines that had
preceded them.

Model E of 1911. The Model E was a
30–60 tractor, the designation indicating
that it produced 30hp at the drawbar and
60hp at the belt. These figures were
substantiated when the Model E was tested
in the 1911 Winnipeg Agricultural Motor
Competition. In 1920 the same tractor was
the subject of Nebraska Tractor Test
Number 8, when the drawbar figure was
measured at almost 50hp and the belt at
more than 75hp. The engine capable of
producing this horsepower was a low-
revving, horizontal twin-cylinder with a
bore and stroke of 25×30cm/10×12in.
The measured fuel consumption of this
engine was high at almost 50 litres/

11 gallons of kerosene per hour. Notable
features of the engine design included the
special carburettor with water injection and
air cooling induced by creating a draught
through the rectangular tower on the front
of the tractor. The company was renamed
the Advance-Rumely Thresher Company in
1915 during the production run of the
Model E 30–60 OilPull, which remained in
production until 1923 when it was
superseded by the similarly designed
20–40 Model G. By 1931, Advance-
Rumely had produced more than 56,500
OilPulls in 14 configurations.

Advance-Rumely, noted for making large
tractors, entered the small tractor market in
1916 when it first advertised its All
Purpose 8–16 model. The operation of the
machine was described as being "just like
handling a horse gang". The machine had
only three wheels – a single steering rear
wheel and two front wheels, one driven and
the other free-wheeling. It was powered by
a four-cylinder engine that ran on kerosene.
The tractor was intended for drawbar towing
of implements and for the belt driving of
machines such as threshers and balers.

While Advance-Rumely continued to
refine its own OilPull line of tractors, it
acquired Aultman Taylor in 1924 but was
itself sold to Allis-Chalmers in 1931. In
that year it marketed the Model 6A tractor,
a modern-looking machine for its time.
The 6A was powered by a six-cylinder
Waukesha engine and fitted with a

■ RIGHT *This large tractor was rated at 22-65hp at the drawbar and belt respectively and was made by the Advance-Rumely Thresher Company during 1919.*

■ BELOW RIGHT *Advance-Rumely was founded by Meinrad Rumely, a German emigrant blacksmith who opened a smithy in La Porte, Indiana in the mid-19th century.*

six-speed gearbox. Allis-Chalmers, however, sold the 6A only until existing stocks had been used up, and less than 1,000 were made in total.

■ **AMERICAN HARVESTER**
American Harvester diesel tractors are made under contract in the People's Republic of China and imported into the United States by a company called Farm Systems International. There are numerous tractor manufacturers in China but Farm Systems International claim to contract only with those manufacturers who are capable of matching or exceeding specified standards of quality and workmanship. The engines used in American Harvester machines incorporate features such as removable cylinder sleeves and forged pistons, aimed at ensuring the longevity of the tractors.

The Model 504 is one of a range of Compact American Harvester tractors that are engineered to last between 6,000 and 11,000 hours between overhauls and are also designed to be sufficiently powerful though small and fuel-efficient. The 504 is fitted with a low-pollution diesel engine coupled to an eight-speed transmission with four-wheel-drive capability. Options include a two-wheel-drive transmission with an adjustable width, row crop front end. The 504 has a full-size, mechanical

■ BELOW *This Advance-Rumely Model H tractor was rated at 16-30hp in 1920, but was superseded by lighter models from 1924.*

power take-off as standard and a full-size, three-point hydraulic hitch. A range of models is available, with engines that produce from 18 to 50hp. All have a 12 volt electrical system with emergency hand crank starting, glow plugs and compression release for cold weather. There is a built-in auxiliary hand-pump to purge fuel lines.

The American Harvester Model 250 is of smaller overall dimensions and is primarily intended for use with implements such as

OTHER MAKES

■ RIGHT *Belarus tractors are made in the Republic of Belarus, a member of the Commonwealth of Independent States previously known as Belorussia, in the former USSR, and are widely exported.*

■ BELOW *Belarus offers six series of tractors from 31 to 180bhp in almost thirty configurations. All the machines are of a simple design to ensure reliability.*

rotary cultivators, rotary disc ploughs, rotary harrows and reaping machines as well as ordinary ploughs and harrows. To enable it to do this it has a system of "live hydraulics" and large diameter tyres to aid traction in fields. It can also be used as the power for irrigation and drainage equipment, threshing machines and rice mills or to drive trailers.

The Model 250 is 268.7cm/105.8in long and 124cm/48.8in wide. The height to steering wheel is 143.3cm/56.4in while the wheel base is 152cm/60in. The turning circle varies depending on whether brakes are fitted to the front axle. With brakes fitted the turning circle is 2.5m/8.25ft while without them it is 2.8m/9.24ft. The Model 250 is powered by a vertical, water cooled, four stroke, three-cylinder diesel. Its displacement is 1432cc/87.4cu in achieved through a bore and stroke of 8.6x9.7cm/ 3.4x3.8in. The Compression Ratio is 22:1 and the engine produces 25hp @ 2500rpm. The engine is cooled by a pressurized system. The transmission has eight forward and two reverse gears and is assembled with a dry, single plate clutch. The gearbox is fitted with a differential lock to assist traction in wet or heavy soil. The drum brake is of the internal expanding shoe type while steering is of a traditional peg and

■ RIGHT *The Belarus 862 D is designed for high speed field work and has a 90hp engine and a four-wheel-drive system that only engages drive to the front axle when the rear wheels slip up to 6 per cent.*

worm design. The Model 250 has 6.0x15
and 8.3x24 tyres, front and rear
respectively and its hydraulic linkage has a
maximum lift capacity of 1878kg/4140lbs.

■ AVANCE

Avance was a Swedish tractor manufacturer
active in the second decade of the 20th
century when tractor innovations were
accruing rapidly. Avance offered a tractor
of an improved design, the first semi-
diesel-engined machine. All oil products
had to be imported into Sweden and were
expensive, so a machine that could run on
as cheap a fuel as possible – including
waste oil – offered clear advantages. The
engineers at Avance had considered the
starting procedure of diesels in some detail
and developed the semi-diesel, which

■ ABOVE RIGHT
*The Belarus 862 D
is fitted with
independent and
ground speed PTO
and category II
live hydraulics
with draught and
position control.*

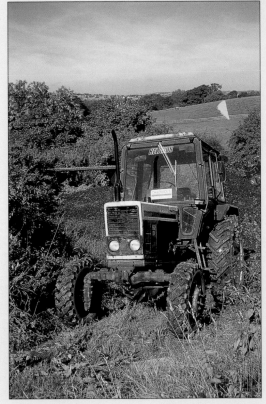

■ RIGHT *The 862
D is powered by a
4075cc/248cu in,
in-line four-cylinder
engine which drives
through a trans-
mission with 18
forward and two
reverse gears.*

ignited the fuel by its injection on to a red
hot bulb in the cylinder head. The Avance
machine offered this new technology in a
machine that was in other ways dated,
relying on both a chassis and tank cooling
of the engine. By the end of the decade
Avance were offering two-cylinder, hot-
bulb, semi-diesel tractors of two capacities,
18–22 and 20–30hp. They utilized
compressed air starters with glow plugs and
batteries as additional options.

■ BELARUS

Belarus Tractors are made in the Minsk
Tractor Factory in the Republic of Belarus,
a member of the Commonwealth of
Independent States (CIS). The company's
products have been exported widely and it
offers numerous tractors in a variety of
configurations.

   The Belarus Model 862 D of 1986 was
powered by an engine that displaced
4075cc/248cu in and produced 90hp. It
featured an automatic, four-wheel-drive
transmission that incorporated 18 forward
and two reverse gears. Hydrostatic steering
was fitted as standard.

   The current Belarus range of four-wheel-
drive tractors includes the 1221, which
produces 130hp, the 115hp 1025, the
105hp 952 and the 862, which produces
90hp. The two-wheel-drive line of Belarus
tractors ranges from the 105hp 950
machine to the 90hp 900 Model.

OTHER MAKES

■ BOLINDER-MUNKTELL

The Swedish tractor-maker Bolinder-Munktell was formed by the amalgamation of two Swedish companies. In 1932 the tractor manufacturer Munktell combined with its engine-maker, Bolinder, to form Bolinder-Munktell, which continued the production of the 15–22 and 20–30 tractors. Munktell is credited with having built the first tractor to be manufactured in Sweden, the BM 30–40 of 1913. It was powered by a two-cylinder Bolinder engine. The company also experimented with wood-burning tractors, because fuel was a major consideration in countries where oil had to be imported. In 1921 and 1922 the company offered a two-stroke, two-cylinder, hot-bulb engine that produced 15-22hp and, as a result, was designated the Model 22. Its engine was actually derived from a marine engine and used compressed air to start after the hot bulbs had been heated with an integral blowlamp. By 1930 the company was also offering a larger model, the 20–30, and both variants took part in the Oxfordshire World Tractor Trials of

■ ABOVE *Bolinder-Munktell later combined with Volvo to form Volvo BM but prior to this the company's two-stroke diesel engines proved popular.*

■ BELOW *Bolinder-Munktell was a merger of the Swedish tractor maker Munktell and engine maker Bolinder. This three-cylinder diesel was one of the company's products.*

1930. Another Swedish manufacturer was Bofors, the arms manufacturer, that entered the tractor market alongside Avance and Munktell with its 40–46hp two-cylinder tractor first built in 1932.

Bolinder-Munktell offered a 31hp twin-cylinder engined tractor in 1939 and in the aftermath of World War II offered the Model 10 tractor, a 23hp machine powered by a hot-bulb engine. It was not until the 1950s that the company abandoned the hot-bulb engine, when it introduced the BM35 and BM55 models with direct injection diesel engines. These tractors also featured five-speed transmissions and an optional cab. Bolinder-Munktell later merged with Volvo.

■ **BRAUD**
In 1870 Braud was founded in St Mars La Jaille, in France, to manufacture threshing machines. Over a century later, in 1975, Braud produced its first grape harvester and went on to specialize in this field. In 1984 Fiatagri acquired 75 per cent of Braud. Then in 1988 all of Fiat-Allis and Fiatagri's activities were merged to form a new company, FiatGeotech, the Fiat group's farm and earthmoving machinery sector. Within this restructuring, Hesston and Braud joined forces in a new company, Hesston-Braud, based in Coex, France. It later became part of New Holland Geotech.

■ **BREDA**
Breda was active in tractor production in Italy during the 1920s, and unlike many of its competitors, produced gasoline-engined tractors. These were powered by four-cylinder engines of 26 and 40hp. During the 1930s the range of models offered was expanded to include both a conventional four-cylinder gasoline/kerosene-engined tractor and an unusual two-stroke, two-cylinder, Junkers diesel-engined machine. After World War II the company offered multi-cylinder-engined crawler tractors.

■ **BROCKWAY**
During the years immediately after World War II, there was an influx of new tractor manufacturers into the industry. Brockway had made bridging equipment for the US

Army during the war and was one of several American companies new to tractor manufacture. Others included Custom, Earthmaster, Farmaster, Friday, General, Harris and Laughlin.

■ **BULL**
The Minneapolis Steel and Machinery Company was primarily a structural steel-maker, producing thousands of tons per year in the late 1800s and early 1900s. The company also manufactured the Corliss steam engine, that served as a power unit for many flour mills in the Dakotas. In 1908, Minneapolis Steel and Machinery produced tractors under the Twin City brand name.

By the outbreak of World War I, the company was one of the larger tractor producers in the world, and had diversified into manufacturing tractors for other companies. One of these was the Bull tractor for the Bull Tractor Co: the company was contracted to build 4,600

machines, using engines supplied by Bull.

The acceptance that small tractors were practical for all kinds of farming tasks quickly changed the emphasis of the tractor-manufacturing industry and threatened some of the old-established companies and their larger machines.

The Bull tractor was a small machine based around a triangular steel frame. It had only one driven wheel, thereby eliminating the need for a differential. A single wheel at the front steered the machine and the other two simply free-wheeled. An opposed twin engine produced up to 12hp and the transmission was as basic as the remainder of the machine, with a single forward and single reverse gear.

At first the little Bull tractor sold well, but after an initial success, the limitations of its usefulness, and some inherent faults in the machine's design and construction became apparent. Sales quickly declined and as a result, little was heard of the company after 1915.

■ ABOVE *This 1950 Bolinder-Munktell BM10 tractor produced 20hp from its two-cylinder, two-stroke hot-bulb engine.*

CASE

■ BELOW *The new Case RC of 1935 was painted light grey in order to distinguish it from the CC models. The RC began production as a four-cylinder, engine-powered, tricycle row crop tractor.*

Case built its first viable gasoline-powered tractor in 1911 and by 1913 had developed a practical and small-sized tractor powered by a gasoline engine, although the company's history began long before this. J. I. Case and Company was formed in 1863, in Racine, Wisconsin, to build steam tractors. It became the J. I. Case Threshing Company in 1880, and its first experimental gasoline tractor appeared in 1892, but was not a success. In 1911 the massive Case 30–60 won first place in the Winnipeg Tractor Trials. It weighed almost 13 tons but clearly found a market, as it was

CASE RC ROW CROP 1935	
Engine	Waukesha in-line four cylinder
Power	18-20hp
Transmission	Three forward speeds, hand clutch
Weight	1180kg/2600lbs

■ BELOW *The Case L model of 1929 ended Case's production of Crossmotor models because the L used an in-line four-cylinder overhead valve engine for propulsion.*

■ RIGHT *The Case CC was a row crop version of the Model C with a distinctive steering arm, nicknamed the "chicken perch" and "fence cutter".*

■ BELOW LEFT *The Case RC of 1939 added the rounded sunburst cast grille and Flambeau Red paintwork.*

■ BELOW RIGHT *Production of Case RC models was moved to Rock Island, Illinois in 1937 after Case had purchased the Rock Island Plow Company.*

made until 1916. A smaller version, the 12–25, was made from 1913 onwards but it was the company's 20–40 model that garnered more awards at the Winnipeg Trials in 1913. All three of these Case tractors were powered by flat twin engines (horizontally opposed twin cylinders) of varying displacements and used other components taken from the Case range of steam engines.

It was generally accepted that the future lay in smaller tractors that had more in common with automobiles than steam engines. Case experimented with small-sized machines and developed the three-wheeled 10–20 Crossmotor tractor. This was powered by a vertical in-line four-cylinder engine mounted transversely across the frame. It had a single driven wheel and an idler wheel on the rear axle. The driven wheel was aligned with the front steering wheel and the machine was capable of pulling a two-tine plough. Between 1915 and 1922 approximately 5,000 10–20s were produced. Case introduced the four-wheeled Model 9–18 in 1916 to compete with the popular Fordson. It was the 9–18 tractor that, in many ways, established Case as a major manufacturer and more than 6,000 of the two versions, 9–18A and 9–18B, had been made by 1919. The 9–18 was a lightweight tractor designed to weigh around the same as a team of horses and capable of pulling a plough or driving a

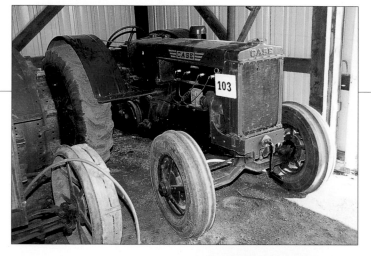

■ LEFT *When pneumatic tyres were still considered innovative, tractor makers offered customers a choice of steel wheels, or pneumatic tyres as used by this Model L.*

Case had not abandoned production of larger tractors altogether and offered the 22–40 between 1919 and 1924 and the 40–72 between 1920 and 1923. Only 42 tractors of the latter design were made. Each weighed 11 tons and when tested in Nebraska in 1923 produced a record 91 belt hp, but used fuel in huge quantities.

A new president, Leon R. Clausen (1878–1965), was appointed to head the

thresher. In 1917 the 10–18 was launched. It was similar to the 9–18 but featured a cast radiator tank and an engine capable of higher rpm. During the 10–18's three-year production run around 9,000 tractors were made. The 15–27 was a tractor designed for a three-tine plough and was the first Case tractor to have a power take-off fitted. Its capabilities matched the requirements of the market to the extent that more than 17,500 were sold between its introduction in 1919 and 1924 when it was superseded by the Model 18–32.

■ LEFT *Later the Case colour scheme was a combination of Flambeau Red and Desert Sand.*

■ BELOW LEFT *The row crop tractors' front wheels minimized crop damage.*

■ BELOW *The refined row crop Case DC included upgrades such as the streamlined cast radiator grille.*

■ RIGHT *The distinctive Case name and logo was always displayed.*

■ FAR RIGHT *What made the Case DEX different from other Case tractors from the early 1940s was that the DEX used the enclosed chain final drive system instead of gears.*

■ BELOW *A 1942 Case DEX model photographed in Yorkshire, England.*

J. I. Case Threshing Machine Company in 1924. Clausen had been born in Fox Lake, Wisconsin and in 1897 had graduated from the University of Wisconsin with a degree in electrical engineering. He had experience of the tractor industry as a former employee of John Deere. He also had an antipathy towards trade unionism and some disdain for customer demands, believing that product design should be solely the province of the engineering department. He started the company working on a redesigned range of tractors.

■ CASE MODEL L

In 1929 the Case Model L went into production based around a unit frame construction. It was notable because, for the first time in 15 years, the engine was not mounted transversely but longitudinally. The angular Model L was a great success and was to remain in

production until 1939 when it was replaced by the Model LA, a restyled and updated version of the L. The restyling gave the tractor a more rounded appearance typical of the time, but much of the engineering was similar to that of the Model L. The engine was a 6.6 litre, overhead valve, in-line, four-cylinder unit. Drive to the rear axle was

by a pair of chains and sprockets as in the Model L. The gearbox was a conventional four-speed unit with a single reverse gear. A lever-operated overcentre-type clutch allowed selection of the required gear. The tractor stayed in production until 1955.

The Case Model C also went into production in 1929 and it, along with

CASE 385 TRACTOR	
Year	1988
Engine	Three cylinder, 2536cc/155cu in
Power	45hp (33.6 kW)
Transmission	Eight forward, four reverse
Weight	(2WD model) 2430kg/5356lbs

■ RIGHT *The Case LA debuted in 1939 although under its streamlined hood and Flambeau red paint it was essentially the earlier Model L tractor, albeit more powerful.*

the Model L, was one of the tractors that helped to establish the Case brand in Great Britain. It was tested in the 1930 World Tractor Trials in Oxfordshire where, in the class for machines fuelled by paraffin, it achieved the best economy figures. The model C recorded a maximum output of 29.8hp on the belt and 21.9hp on the drawbar, figures that were almost identical to those achieved in Nebraska the previous year. The results of the tests were widely advertised by Case, which later offered the Models CC, CI, CO, CV and CD (row crop, industrial, orchard, vineyard and crawler versions respectively). Under

■ BELOW *This is a 1943 version of the Case LA tractor, which had revised wheels over the initial model. The LA was designed to pull up to five ploughs.*

■ ABOVE *The plate that identifies the tractor as Case model number 11161 LA also bears the "Old Abe" mascot and is positioned next to the oil pressure gauge.*

■ LEFT *Despite the distinctive green and yellow colour scheme that suggests John Deere, the French company SFV was acquired by Case during the 1960s.*

CASE MX100C	
Year	1998
Engine	4 litre four-cylinder turbo
Power	75 kW at 2200rpm
Transmission	16 forward, 12 reverse
Weight	4750kg/10,470lbs

Clausen, progress and innovation were cautious and conservative which, in some instances allowed competitors to benefit at Case's expense. One area in which Clausen wanted to advance the company was to offer a full line of implements to complement the tractor range. To this end, Case bought out Emerson-Brantingham in 1928 and the Rock Island Plow Company in 1937. Following these acquisitions, and that of the Showers Brothers furniture factory in

Burlington, Iowa, Case moved towards production of combine harvesters. A new line of tractors appeared in 1939, the Models D and DC, which were to be followed by the Models S and V and an upgraded Model L, the LA.

The Model D was a four-wheeled tractor and was designed to pull a three-tine plough. It had a belt pulley, PTO and Case's motor lift system for the implements. The DC was a row crop tricycle with adjustable wheel spacing

■ ABOVE RIGHT *Société Française Vierzon (SFV) incorporated the blue, white and red of the French tricolour in its company logo, seen here on the right-hand side of the 302 model.*

■ RIGHT *The two-stroke semi-diesel SFV tractors featured distinctively shaped exhausts, and a transverse, leaf-sprung beam front axle.*

■ RIGHT *Case pioneered the loader backhoe to be sold as a single unit in the late 1950s and had considerable success with the resultant versatile machine. This is a 1990s version, the Case 580 SK.*

and what the manufacturers termed "quick-dodge" steering for close cultivation in uneven rows. The D Series tractors were the first Case machines to be painted in a bright hue – Flambeau Red – a colour that was to become standard for the next decade.

■ **THE 1940S**

As it did for most American industry, World War II changed things for Case. Between 1940 and 1945 three Case plants had made in excess of 1.3 million 155mm howitzer shells. Case also made specialized military tractors such as the Model LA1. Alongside these projects, Case made parts for army trucks, amphibious tracked vehicles and military aircraft. This war production did not adversely affect Case's tractor sales to farmers at a time when agricultural production was as crucial as armament production; in fact it ended the effects of the Depression on the company. Labour relations were not all that they might have been and in 1945 Case employees from the Racine plant went on strike for 440 days, the longest strike in the company's history. This had a disastrous effect on Case's dealers and customer base and has been credited by many historians as one of the reasons for John Deere's growth and consolidation of its position within the tractor market.

In the aftermath of both the war and the strikes, Case looked towards expansion. The company bought plants in Bettendorf, Iowa and Stockton, California, as well as the Kilby Steel Company of Anniston, Alabama. With these additional facilities Case sought to produce a wider range of farm machinery, including combine harvesters, rakes, ploughs and manure spreaders. The Alabama plant was to be used for the production of new machines, including tobacco harvesters for the south-east of the United States. In the wake of this expansion came a slump in profits for the years 1950–53, largely because many innovations that were being adopted by rival manufacturers – including the three-point hitch – were not offered on Case

■ ABOVE *The SFV 201 was one of the models made by SFV prior to the company's acquisition by Case.*

■ LEFT *Prior to the acquisition, SFV specialized in the production of two-stroke, semi-diesel engined tractors of an unusual design that proved popular in Europe.*

■ LEFT *A Case tractor towing a Massey-Ferguson baler during haymaking on a hill farm in Yorkshire, England.*

machines. An example of this failure to compete can be seen in Case's baling machines; in 1941 the company dominated the hay baler market because its baler had been the first to pick up the hay as it was towed along. Just before the outbreak of war New Holland introduced a baler that used twine instead of wire for baling and, more importantly, did not require two extra men to tie bales as the Case machine did. Case failed to make any improvements to its balers and sales slumped to the extent that in 1953 Case achieved only 5 per cent of sales.

■ BELOW *A four-wheel-drive tractor from the Case XL Series towing a disc harrow in a field in Normandy, France.*

■ JOHN T. BROWN

The company was in the doldrums and the situation was exacerbated when Clausen relinquished the presidency in 1948 and was succeeded by Theodore Johnson. Johnson resigned in 1953 to be replaced by John T. Brown. This change, along with impetus from the company's underwriter and a more dynamic board of directors, began to turn the company's fortunes around. New engineering practices and an acceptance

of diesel engines, as well as new lines of implements including one-way disc ploughs, cotton strippers, disc harrows, Lister press drills and front loaders, all took the company forward. Most important among these advances was the

500 Series of tractors. This new line was soon followed by the 400 and the 300 Series.

These ranges of tractors were effectively the first completely redesigned Case models to appear since

■ RIGHT *The 1056XL is the largest model in the Case IH 56 Series. It is powered by a six-cylinder engine that produces 98hp and features a four-wheel-drive transmission.*

the 1930s. The 500 models of 1953 were powered by an in-line, six-cylinder, diesel engine that developed sufficient horsepower to pull five plough bottoms. The 500 also featured power steering, a push-button starter and live hydraulics, making them easy to operate. The 400 Series was unveiled in 1955 and incorporated all Case's new technology. Power came from an in-line four-cylinder engine with a choice of diesel, gasoline or LPG fuel, capable of pulling four ploughs. Final drive was now by means of gears and the transmission had eight forward speeds. A hydraulic vane steering system was fitted, as were a three-point hitch and suspension seat for the driver. The 400 Series models were the first made by the company to be advertised on television. Both the 400 and 500 Series models were made at the Racine, Wisconsin plant, and a third new model line was made at Rock Island and went on sale in 1956.

■ THE 300 SERIES

The 300 Series offered customers considerable choice: diesel or gasoline engine, and transmission with four, eight or twelve speeds. The other new feature of the 300 Series was its streamlined styling, which soon became the norm across Case's entire range. The next development in styling came in 1957 and was inspired by the automobile industry: the radiator grille was squared off and

CASE 1255XL 1990	
Engine	Six cylinder turbo 5867cc/358cu in
Power	25hp/92kw
Transmission	20 x 9 syncromesh
Weight	6225kg/13,720lbs

■ BELOW *The Case IH 1255XL, seen here harvesting, has a two speed PTO that produces 121.1hp @ 540rpm and 1000 rpm. The hydraulic system has a maximum pressure of 175kg/sq cm (2488lb/sq in).*

inclined forwards at the top, giving a slightly concave appearance. This styling continued through the Case-O-Matics and the 30 Series tractors, introduced in 1960, and even to the massive 1200 Traction King first produced in 1964.

■ ACQUISITIONS

In France, SFV – Société Française Vierzon – had entered the tractor market in 1935 with a machine not unlike the Lanz Bulldog. Despite World War II the company endured until 1960, when it was acquired by Case. In 1957 Case merged with the American Tractor Corporation, based in Churubusco, Indiana. This corporation manufactured "Terratrac" crawler tractors and Case continued production of such machines in Indiana until 1961 when it moved the production to Burlington, Iowa. One of the results of this merger was the

■ RIGHT *Tractors such as the Case IH 4230 have a forward tilting hood and swing out service panel to enable convenience of maintenance.*

■ BOTTOM *The Case 5150 is one of many tractors equipped with front weights which are positioned to improve traction as well as reducing turning radius.*

■ BELOW *Modern tractors such as this Case XL Plus model are fitted with transmissions that have up to 16 forward speeds as well as, in this case, a driven front axle.*

development of the loader/backhoe. Case's 320 loader/backhoe was the first such machine to be built and marketed as a single unit.

■ **CHANGING TIMES**
Case took over the British tractor-maker, David Brown Ltd, in 1972. This acquisition was seen as more than a purchase because the British company had a large distribution network in Great Britain, outlets in Europe, and even some in the United States. From then on David Brown tractors would be painted in David Brown White and Case Red. The ownership of Case itself had changed in the late 1960s. The Kern County Land Company was a majority shareholder in Case and in 1967 this company was acquired by Tenneco Inc from Texas. In 1974 new agricultural products from Case included the 2670 Traction King tractor, the 6000 Series of mouldboard ploughs and the F21 Series

of wheeled tandem-disc harrows. A year later the 1410 and 1412 tractors appeared. There were further new tractors the following year, when the 1570 Agri-King and 2870 Traction King 300hp four-wheel-drive machines were announced. As it was America's bicentennial year Case also offered a limited-edition version of the Model 1570, known as the Spirit of '76. The 70 and 90 Series tractors were new for 1978 and were followed by another new line in 1983, the 94 Series.

In 1985 Tenneco Inc completed its purchase of International Harvester,

after that company had been adversely affected by the recession in farming in the early 1980s. In a restructuring of Tenneco, Case IH became Tenneco's largest division. The Case IH range for 1986 included the Model 685L, with a four-cylinder engine that developed 69hp, an eight forward speed and two reverse 4x4 transmission and hydrostatic steering. A larger model in the same range was the Model 1594, with an in-line six-cylinder engine that produced 96hp and drove through a four-range, semi-automatic, Hydra-Shift transmission.

A decade after the restructuring Tenneco formed the Case Corporation and sold its agricultural products as Case IH machines. The current Case IH range includes Magnum and Maxxum tractors. The 8900 Magnum Series Tractors are powered by an 8300cc/506cu in displacement engine and assembled with an 18-speed Powershift

■ BELOW *The MX Series cabs are quiet with a 72dB(A) limit. The temperature is controlled and the air in the cab filtered.*

■ LEFT *The 1998 Case MX120 has sixteen forward gears, four wheel drive and hydrostatic steering.*

transmission. There are four models in the MX Series of Maxxum tractors, with outputs ranging from 85 to 115 PTO hp. They are suited to a variety of tasks including tillage, planting and loader work. They are also designed to adapt to speciality row crop, hay, forage and utility applications. The MX100 offers 85 PTO hp, while the MX135 produces 115 PTO hp. The Maxxum Series is fitted with a modern design of six-cylinder 5883cc/359cu in displacement turbocharged diesel engine. The Maxxum tractor transmission is a 16-speed fully synchronized unit and is standard on all models except on the

MX 135, which has a Powershift transmission. Standard creeper and super creeper transmissions are available on all models. A compact series of three Maxxum tractors is also offered: Models MX80C, 90C and 100C. Alongside these are the CS 110-150 and CX50 to CX100 Models. A specialized agricultural machine manufactured by Case IH at its East Moline plant is the 2555 Cotton Express, a state-of-the-art cotton picker. Cotton picking is a specialized business and the machines designed for it have become increasingly technical. The 2555 is capable of holding up to 3855kg/

8500lb of cotton and has a 32.5cu m/1150cu ft vertical lift basket. The design of components, such as straight-through front and rear outlets, are intended to enhance crop flow, reduce chokes, improve drum component life and decrease wear on moistener pads and pad holders. The 2555 is powered by a 260hp turbocharged diesel engine and offers on-road transport speeds of around 29kph/18mph as well as sufficient power for harvesting. A more conventional, but no less technologically advanced, combine harvester currently made by Case IH is the Axial-Flow 2100 Series.

■ LEFT *This 1998 Case MX tractor is equipped with a Miller PL-3 front loader, a versatile tractor attachment.*

■ OPPOSITE *Despite its apparent complexity the three-point linkage and hydraulic system on the rear of this Case IH tractor is similar to the one devised by Harry Ferguson.*

■ LEFT *The front loader, such as the unit attached to this Case tractor, is suited to a variety of farming tasks including the handling and loading of crops.*

■ WORLD PRODUCTION

Towards the end of the millennium, the Case Corporation is multinational. In North America it has numerous production facilities, each dedicated to specific products. In Burlington, Iowa, loaders, backhoes, forklifts, crawlers, dozers and hydraulic cylinders are produced. In East Moline, Illinois, the company manufactures combine harvesters, cotton pickers, grain and corn heads while in Fargo, North Dakota, the Case plant produces tractors, wheeled loaders and Concord air drills.

In the same state a plant in Valley City is dedicated to electronics. In Hamilton, Ontario, tillage, crop production and material handling equipment are made. In Racine, Wisconsin, Case produces its lines of Magnum and Maxxum tractors as well as transmissions and foundry products. Skid steer and trenching machines are made in Wichita, Kansas and directional drills are fabricated in Hugo, Minnesota. The company has numerous plants around Europe: St Valentin, Austria, is where Steyr tractors are made, while excavators, loaders and backhoes are produced in Crépy-en-Valois, France.

Another French plant at Croix produces agricultural and construction equipment cabs, while others at St Dizier and Tracy-le-Mont produce transmissions and hydraulic cylinders

respectively. In Britain, tractors, gears and shafts are made in Doncaster, mini-excavators and skid steer machines in Manchester and sprayers are made in Lincoln. Forage harvesters, combines and square balers are produced in Neustadt, Germany. In South America, a plant in Sorocaba, Brazil, makes wheeled loaders, backhoes and excavators.

Case also has a factory in Australia in Bundaberg, Queensland, that produces Austoft sugar cane harvesters, transporters and planters. The corporation participates in a number of

joint ventures, including those with Hay & Forage Industries of Hesston, Kansas, that produces hay and forage equipment, and the Consolidated Diesel Company of Rocky Mount, North Carolina, that makes engines.

Further afield, Case works with the Liuzhou Case Liugong Construction Equipment Company Ltd of Liuzhou, China, to make loaders and backhoes. Case has a similar arrangement with Brastoft Maquinas e Sistemas Agroindustrias SA in Piracicaba, Brazil, to produce sugar cane harvesters, and with UzCaseMash in Tashkent, Uzbekistan where cotton pickers are made. Case's East Moline, Illinois plant produces combine harvesters, cotton pickers, grain heads and corn heads, while its Fargo, North Dakota facility builds tractors and wheeled loaders as well as making Concord air drills. Case's 1997 revenue amounted to approximately $6 billion and the corporation has about 18,000 employees and 4,900 dealers and distributors.

CATERPILLAR

■ BELOW *The Caterpillar Sixty was one of the models of crawler manufactured in the Peoria, Illinois plant from 1925 onwards. It was a post-merger version of the Best 60hp model crawler.*

During the late 19th century Benjamin Holt and Daniel Best experimented with various forms of steam tractors for use in farming. They did so independently, running separate companies, but both were pioneers with track-type tractors and gasoline-powered tractor engines. Paralleling the developments of the steam excavator were experiments with tracked machines referred to as "crawlers". Crawler technology would later diverge into separate and distinct strands of activity, although the technology employed remained essentially the same. One of these strands of activity is, of course, the crawler's agricultural application.

The initial experiments involved wheeled steam tractors which were converted to run with tracks to overcome the problem of wheels sinking into soft ground. The first test of such a machine took place in November 1904 in Stockton, California, where a Holt steam tractor had been converted to run on tracks. This was accomplished by the removal of the rear wheels and their replacement with tracks made from a series of 7.5 × 10cm/3 × 4in wooden blocks 60cm/2ft long, bolted to a linked steel chain which ran around smaller wheels, a driven sprocket and idler on each side. Originally the machine was steered by a single tiller wheel, although this system was later dropped in favour of the idea of disengaging drive to one track by means of a clutch which slewed the machine around. From here it was but a short step to gasoline-powered crawlers, one of which was constructed by Holt in 1906. By 1908, 28 Holt gasoline-powered crawlers were engaged in work on the Los Angeles Aqueduct project in the Tehachapi mountains – something Holt saw as a

proving-ground for his machines. By 1915, Holt "Caterpillar" track-type tractors were being used by the Allies in World War I.

In the years after World War I, the Best Company continued the work with crawler-tracked machinery. In 1921 it introduced a new machine, the Best 30 Tracklayer. This crawler was fitted with a light-duty bulldozer blade, was powered by an internal combustion engine and had an enclosed cab. At this time there was a considerable amount of litigation involving patents and types of tracklayers, and two companies were frequently named in the litigation: Best and Holt. Holt held a patent for track-layers which put him in a position to charge a licence fee to other manufacturers of the time, including Monarch, Bates and Cletrac. During World War I, much of Holt's production went to the US Army, while Best supplied farmers. After the war the two companies competed in all markets and neither had a significant

advantage over the other. Eventually in 1925, the Holt and Best companies effectively merged to form the Caterpillar Tractor Company. Holt had in fact bought out Daniel Best in 1908 but later had to compete with Best's son, C. L. "Leo" Best.

In late 1925 the new Caterpillar Company published prices for its product line: the Model 60 sold for $6,050, the Model 30 for $3,665 and the two ton for $1,975. The consolidation of the two brands into one company proved its value in the next few years: the prices of the big tracklayers were cut, business increased and sales more than doubled.

The Caterpillar Twenty was a mid-sized crawler tractor put into production by the company in Peoria, Illinois late in 1927; production continued until 1933. It was powered by an in-line four-cylinder engine that made 25hp at 1250rpm. According to its makers it could pull 2174kg/4793lb at the

■ RIGHT *A Caterpillar crawler being used for orchard work. The operator is wearing protective clothes to protect himself from the effects of pesticides.*

■ BELOW *A 1950s Caterpillar D4 with dozer blade; the "D" prefix indicates a diesel engine.*

drawbar in first gear, but in the respected Nebraska Tractor Tests it recorded a maximum pull of 2753kg/6071lb. The transmission was a three-speed with a reverse, and steering was achieved through multi-plate disc clutches and contracting band brakes. With a width of only 1.5m/5ft and length of 2.7m/9ft the tractor was compact and helped to establish Caterpillar as a known brand on smaller farms and in export markets. In 1929 the company announced the Caterpillar 15, which increased its range of crawlers to five models of varying capabilities.

In 1931 the first Diesel Sixty-Five

Tractor rolled off the new assembly line in East Peoria, Illinois, with a new, efficient source of power for track-type tractors. This year also saw the shift to the now familiar yellow livery of Caterpillar products; all Caterpillar machinery left the factory painted Highway Yellow, which was seen both as a way of brightening up the machines in an attempt to lift the gloom of the Depression, and as a safety measure since machines increasingly being used in road construction had to be visible to motorists. Highway Yellow caught on slowly at first but eventually became the standard colour for all construction

equipment. New diesel-engined crawlers went into production in 1935. Their model designations began with RD – Rudolph Diesel's initials – and finished with a number that related to the crawler's size and engine power, so that RD8, RD7 and RD6 machines were soon followed by the RD4 of 1936. (Other accounts of where RD comes from have suggested that the R stands for Roosevelt and the D for Diesel.)

The RD8 was capable of 95 drawbar hp, while the RD7 achieved 70 drawbar

CATERPILLAR RD7	
Year	1937
Engine	Four cylinder diesel
Power	61hp at 850rpm
Transmission	Three speed
Weight	9535kg/21,020lbs

hp and the RD6 45 drawbar hp. By this time the US Forest Service was using machines such as the Cletrac Forty with an angled blade on the front, so Caterpillar built one fitted with a LaPlante-Choate Trailblazer blade. Ralph Choate specialized in building blades to be fastened to the front of other people's crawlers: his first one was used on road construction work between Cedar Rapids and Dubuque, Iowa.

In 1938, Caterpillar started production of its smallest crawler tractor, the D2. It was designed for agricultural use and was capable of pulling three- or four-tine ploughs or a disc harrow. The Nebraska tests rated it as having 19.4 drawbar hp and 27.9 belt hp. A variation of the D2 was the gasoline- or paraffin-powered R2, which offered similar power output.

By 1940 the Caterpillar product line included motor graders, blade graders, elevating graders, terracers and electrical generating sets and by 1942 Caterpillar track-type tractors, motor graders, generator sets and a special engine for the M4 tank were being used by the United States in its war effort. The agricultural applications of the larger Caterpillar diesel crawlers such

as the D7 and D8 Models tended to be reserved for huge farms, where multiple implements could be used. The widespread use of Caterpillar products during World War II led the company to shift the emphasis of its operations towards construction in the post-war years. In 1950 the Caterpillar Tractor Co. Ltd was established in Great Britain, the first of many overseas operations created to help manage foreign exchange shortages, tariffs and import controls and to improve service to customers around the world. In 1953 the company created a separate sales and marketing division just for engine customers. Since then, the Engine Division has become important in the

diesel engine market and accounts for one quarter of the company's total sales albeit not wholly in agricultural applications.

In 1963 Caterpillar and Mitsubishi Heavy Industries Ltd formed one of the first joint ventures in Japan to involve partial US ownership. Caterpillar-Mitsubishi Ltd started production in 1965 and was subsequently renamed Shin Caterpillar Mitsubishi Ltd, becoming the second largest maker of construction and mining equipment in Japan. Caterpillar Financial Services Corporation was formed in 1981 to offer equipment financing options to customers worldwide. During the early 1980s the worldwide recession took its

■ RIGHT *The Caterpillar Challenger tractors have found wide acceptance for farming around the globe. This one is seen working in Zambia, Africa.*

toll on Caterpillar, costing the company the equivalent of US $1 million a day and forcing it to reduce employment dramatically. During the later years of that decade the product line continued to be diversified, and this led the company back towards agricultural products. In 1987 the rubber-tracked crawler machines named Challengers appeared in fields, offering a viable alternative to wheeled tractors.

The Caterpillar range for 1996 included a model known as the Challenger 75C. Its engine displaces 10 litres/629cu in and produces a maximum power of 325hp. The operating weight is in excess of 16 tons.

It is fitted with rubber crawler tracks known as Mobil-trac. The company continued to expand, acquiring the UK-based Perkins Engines in 1997. With the addition of Germany's MaK Motoren the previous year, Caterpillar became the world leader in diesel engine manufacturing. In the same year the company also diversified into the compact machine business, to offer a range of versatile small construction machines.

Considerable innovative technology is employed in the assembly of agricultural crawlers. The undercarriage is designed to transfer maximum engine power to the drawbar. Because there is less slip with

tracks than wheels the crawler will do more work with less horsepower and requires less fuel to do so. Traction under heavy loads is a variable; a wheeled tractor typically experiences slip levels of up to 15 per cent while under the same heavy drawbar loads, a Challenger tractor with Mobil-trac technology experiences up to 4 per cent slip. The long, narrow footprint of the rubber crawler tracks allows the operator to get into the field in difficult conditions by lowering ground pressure and increasing flotation. By distributing the gross weight over more axles, Caterpillar's crawlers and combines achieve reduced soil compaction.

■ RIGHT *The Challenger crawler models use what the makers term Mobil-trac, a type of rubber track technology that offers advantages in traction and flotation over wheeled types.*

DAVID BROWN

■ BELOW *The successful Cropmaster tractors were superseded by the 25 and 30 models, available in gasoline or diesel.*

David Brown manufactured Ferguson tractors in the mid-1930s as a result of Harry Ferguson approaching the company then known as David Brown Gear Cutters of Huddersfield, England, with a view to the manufacture of a tractor transmission. Brown was noted for the manufacture of gears and Harry Ferguson wanted to produce a tractor with an American Hercules engine and an innovative hydraulic lift. This machine came to be built by Brown at a plant in Meltham, near Huddersfield, after the prototype had been tested. Known as the Ferguson Model, it was at first fitted with a Coventry Climax engine and subsequently with an engine of Brown's own design. Production ceased in 1939 because Brown wanted to increase its power and Ferguson to reduce the costs.

■ DAVID BROWN VAK-1

Harry Ferguson travelled to the United States to see Henry Ford while David Brown exhibited a new model of a tractor built to his own design. The new machine was the VAK-1 and featured an

■ BELOW *The successful Cropmaster tractors were superseded by the 25 and 30 models, available in gasoline or diesel.*

■ BELOW *The Cropmaster was introduced in 1947 as the replacement for the successful VAK-1 and VAK-1a models.*

■ BELOW *A restored David Brown tractor on display within a few miles of the original David Brown factory in Meltham, England.*

■ ABOVE *A farmer driving a restored David Brown Cropmaster: the raised windshield was intended to divert cold winds away from the driver's hands.*

■ RIGHT *Farmers with a David Brown Cropmaster during a break in the ploughing competitions at the noted Great Dorset Steam Fair held annually in England.*

DAVID BROWN VAK-1	
Year	1939
Engine	2.5 litre four cylinder
Power	35bhp @ 2000rpm
Transmission	Four forward gears
Weight	1625kg/3585lbs

■ LEFT *The David Brown company was initially a gear manufacturer, but went on to make tractors with Harry Ferguson.*

hydraulic lift. After World War II the Yorkshire-based company reintroduced the VAK-1 in a slightly improved version, the VAK-1a, until it launched the Cropmaster of 1947. This became a popular machine, especially the diesel form which was introduced in 1949.

David Brown unveiled the Model 2D at the 1955 Smithfield Agricultural Show. This was a small tractor designed for small-scale farming and row crop work. Only about 2,000 were made during a six-year production run which

■ LEFT *Ben Addy's restored David Brown 880. The 880 was one of the restyled models of a design that was introduced with the 900 model of 1956. The 880 superseded the 950 in 1962.*

■ RIGHT *The driver's eye view from the seat of the later version of the David Brown 880 tractor.*

■ BELOW *The 880 designation endured and is found on this later David Brown tractor. The bar behind the driver's seat is to protect the driver if there was a rollover when working on hillsides.*

accounted for a significant percentage of the market which the model was aimed at. Unconventionally, the air-cooled two-cylinder diesel engine was positioned behind the driver and the implements were operated from a mid-mounted tool carrier, operated by a compressed air system. The air was contained within the tractor's tubular frame.

■ **DAVID BROWN 950**

The styling of David Brown tractors remained closely based on the rounded VAK series until 1956, when the new 900 tractor was unveiled. The 900 offered the customer a choice of four

DAVID BROWN 950 TRACTOR	
Year	1958
Engine	four cylinder diesel or petrol option
Power	42.5hp
Transmission	Four forward speeds
Weight	n/k

■ RIGHT *A David Brown tractor fitted with a cab and a David Brown manufactured, hydraulically operated front loading shovel.*

■ BELOW RIGHT *A David Brown 995. David Brown was later acquired by Case.*

■ BELOW *A David Brown with a rotary hay rake during harvest in West Yorkshire, England. While David Browns were exported worldwide, this one never went more than ten miles from the factory where it was made.*

engines, but its production run lasted only until 1958 when the 950 was announced. This tractor was available in both diesel and gasoline forms, both rated at 42.5hp. The specification of the 950 was upgraded during the four-year production run, with improvements such as an automatic depth-control device being added to the hydraulics and a dual speed power take-off being introduced. A smaller model, the 850, was also available from 1960 onwards as a 35hp diesel. It stayed in production until it was replaced by the three-cylinder diesel 770 in 1965. During this period approximately 2000 Oliver tractors were also produced by David Brown in its Meltham factory for the Oliver Corporation. The David Brown company was taken over by Case in 1972.

OTHER MAKES

(Deutz, Eagle, Emerson-Brantingham)

■ DEUTZ

The company that became known as Deutz was among the pioneers of the internal combustion engine. Nikolaus August Otto, in conjunction with Eugen Langen, manufactured a four-stroke engine which the duo exhibited in Paris at the World Exhibition of 1867. The pair formed a company, Gasmotoren Fabrik Deutz AG, and employed the likes of Gottlieb Daimler and Wilhelm Maybach.

The company introduced its first tractor and motor plough, considered to be of advanced design, in 1907. In 1926 Deutz unveiled the MTZ 222 diesel tractor and the diesel tractor technology race was under way.

In Germany the diesel engine changed the face of tractor manufacture, and at the beginning of the 1930s, Deutz produced its Stahlschlepper ("Iron Tractor") models including the F1M 414, F2M 317 and F3M 315, with single-, twin- and three-cylinder diesel engines respectively. The smaller engines were started by an electrical mechanism while the larger one started with compressed air. When running, the largest displacement model produced 50hp. By this time Deutz was selling its engines to other tractor makers, including Fahr, with which it later merged. Ritscher was another company that used Deutz diesels in the construction of what was the only

tricycle-type tractor built in Germany.

After World War II, Deutz became Klockner-Humboldt-Deutz AG, acquired Fahr and offered air-cooled diesel tractors such as the Models 514 and 612. The company was among the first European

■ ABOVE *The lack of a radiator in the post-war Deutz meant the round front panel gave a distinctive appearance.*

■ LEFT *A four-wheel-drive Deutz-Fahr: Deutz acquired Fahr after World War II.*

■ BELOW LEFT *In the post-war years European tractors were considerably less advanced and less complex than those from the United States.*

■ BELOW RIGHT *This Deutz is equipped with PTO and drawbar!*

manufacturers to export its tractors to the United States. It also built tractors in South America and acquired a share of Steiger. In 1985 Deutz purchased Allis-Chalmers and formed Deutz-Allis, which later became part of the AGCO Corporation.

■ ABOVE LEFT *A diesel-engined Deutz 7206 tractor. This is a two-wheel-drive model so does not have open centre front tyres, but ribbed ones to assist steering.*

■ ABOVE RIGHT *This Deutz-Fahr DX 6.31 is four-wheel drive and so has open centre tyres that enhance traction at the front axle.*

■ BELOW *This Deutz-Fahr Agcotion shows the latest in tractor cab styling. The front ballast weights enhance traction at the front axle of the four-wheel-drive model.*

■ **EAGLE**

The Eagle Manufacturing Company was based in Appleton, Wisconsin and started tractor manufacture in 1906 with a horizontally opposed twin-cylinder engine powered machine. By 1911 it was producing a four-cylinder 56hp machine and by 1916 had a range of four-cylinder tractors in production that took it through the 1920s. In 1930 it changed course and moved from flat twins to vertical in-line six-cylinder machines. One of these was the 6A Eagle, designed for three- to four-

plough use and powered by a Waukesha six-cylinder engine that produced 22 belt hp and 37 drawbar hp. Model 6B was a row crop machine and 6C a utility tractor. The Eagle stayed in production in its various forms until World War II when production ceased, not to be resumed.

■ **EMERSON-BRANTINGHAM**

Emerson-Brantingham was one of the pioneers of American agricultural machinery manufacturing, with roots that stretched back to John H. Manny's reaper of 1852. The company had purchased the Gas Traction Company of Minneapolis in 1912 and became heavily involved in the manufacture of gasoline-engined tractors. Its range included the Big 4 Model 30, a 30 drawbar hp 10 ton machine that was subsequently enlarged into the Big 4 Model 45. This was rated at 45 belt hp and 90 drawbar hp and was even heavier. The Model 20 of 1913 was a much smaller machine and this was followed by the Model AA 12-20 of 1918 that, in turn, was refined into the Model K of 1925.

The huge company, which was based in Rockford, Illinois, was facing financial difficulties in 1928 when it was bought by Case. This acquisition gave Case a boost as it acquired valuable sales territory in the heart of America's corn belt through a well-established dealer network, in addition to a proven line of farm implements.

Case later dropped the Emerson-Brantingham line of tractors but retained many of its implements.

FENDT

One of the simplest tractors available in Germany during the 1930s was the Fendt Dieselross, or "diesel horse". It was little more than a stationary engine equipped with a basic transmission system and wheels. During World War II Fendt was among the German tractor manufacturers that developed gas generator-powered tractors that would burn almost any combustible material in response to the fuel shortages of the war. In the post-war years Fendt reintroduced its Dieselross tractors in different capacities. A 25hp version was powered by an MWM twin-cylinder engine, while a 16hp model used a Deutz engine. Fendt was acquired by the AGCO corporation in 1997.

■ ABOVE RIGHT *A 1928 Fendt machine designed for mowing grass. It is powered by a single cylinder engine fuelled with benzine, and was assembled by Johann Georg Fendt and his son Hermann.*

■ RIGHT *A 1992 four-wheel-drive Fendt Farmer 312 tractor ploughing an English field in heavy conditions.*

■ BELOW *A 1932 Fendt Dieselross with a sidebar mower. This tractor was powered by a 1000cc/60cu in displacement single cylinder Deutz diesel engine.*

FENDT FARMER 312	
Year	1998
Engine	In-line six cylinder turbo diesel
Power	110 PTO hp, 125 BS hp
Transmission	21 forward, 21 reverse
Weight	2363kg/5210lbs

■ ABOVE *A four-wheel-drive Fendt Farmer Turbomatik, working with rollers, during the field cultivation process.*

■ LEFT *The Dieselross name was used by Fendt on several of its tractors. This 1952 model had a diminutive MWM single cylinder diesel engine of 850cc/52cu in displacement, and six forward gears.*

■ BELOW *Fendt used the Farmer designation on several models of its tractors through the decades. This is a Farmer 45 model which contrasts with the Turbomatik at the top of the page.*

■ ABOVE *A 1950s Fendt Farmer 2D diesel tractor with a two axled drawbar trailer, loaded up with logs.*

FERGUSON

The Ferguson tractor evolved from an arrangement made with David Brown and later a partnership between Harry Ferguson and Henry Ford. Originally, Harry Ferguson, who came from Belfast, had installed his innovative three-point hitching system on David Brown tractors. He subsequently made a deal with Henry Ford, through their famous "handshake agreement", although Ford and Ferguson later went their separate ways. This split led to a certain amount of litigation when Ferguson opened his own Detroit factory. The lawsuit which followed suggested that Ford's use of the Ferguson System on its 8N tractors was considered a violation of Harry's patent. The upshot was that Ferguson won

■ ABOVE *The Ferguson-Brown tractor was manufactured in the latter part of the 1930s, through the collaboration of Harry Ferguson and David Brown. Only 1350 tractors were made.*

■ LEFT *A Ferguson TE20 at work in an English field with a Massey-Harris baler. The TE20 went into production in 1946 and became a familiar sight on British farms.*

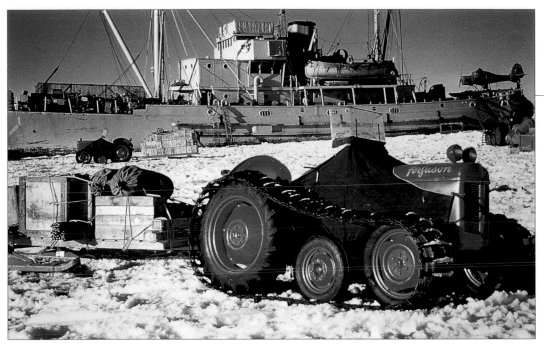

FERGUSON-BROWN TYPE A	
Year	1936
Engine	Coventry Climax E Series four cylinder
Power	18 – 20hp
Transmission	Three forward, one reverse
Weight	n/k

■ ABOVE *Ferguson tractors, converted to full track configuration for the Commonwealth Expedition to the South Pole in the Antarctic, unloading stores.*

■ BELOW LEFT *Over 300,000 TE20s were manufactured in the production run of the TE20, which paralleled production of the TO20 in the United States.*

■ BELOW *The TE20 was marketed under a slogan that read, "It's what the implement does that sells the tractor". This is a 1949 model.*

■ BELOW *TE20 Fergusons were initially available with a gasoline engine but later diesel and TVO - Tractor Vaporising Oil - versions were made available. This is a 1955 TVO model.*

■ OPPOSITE *A Ferguson TE20 ploughing the fields with a two-bottom Ferguson plough, connected to the tractor by means of Ferguson's revolutionary three-point linkage.*

FORD FERGUSON 9N	
Year	1939
Engine	1965cc/120cu in displacement four cylinder
Power	16.31 drawbar and 23.56 belt hp
Transmission	Three speed
Weight	n/k

■ LEFT *A 1951 TED20. At this time production of the TE models was often in excess of 500 per week.*

■ RIGHT *The TE20 inspired great affection and was renowned for its reliability and capacity for hard work.*

damages for patent infringement and loss of business from Ford.

Now on his own, Harry Ferguson set about making his own line of tractors, the TE and TO models. TE was an acronym for Tractor England while TO stood for Tractor Overseas. Both models were not dissimilar to the Fordson 9N but the Ferguson model featured a more powerful engine and a fourth gear ratio. Harry Ferguson came to an arrangement with Sir John Black of the Standard Motor Company in Britain to produce a new tractor in his factory in Coventry. Production started in 1946, using an imported Continental engine. Standard's own engine was substituted when it became available in 1947, with a diesel option being offered in 1951. The first Ferguson was the TE20, referred to as the TO20 in the United States. Over 500,000 TE20s were built in Britain from 1946–56, while some 60,000 TO20s were built in the United States during 1948–51. This tractor – the TE20 – was nicknamed the "Grey Fergy", a reference both to its designer and to its drab paintwork. It became enormously popular, to the extent of being ubiquitous on British farms. In August 1951, Harry released the TO30 Series, and the TO35, painted beige and metallic green, came out in 1954. Ferguson sold his company to Massey-Harris in 1953.

■ FERGUSON RESEARCH

Harry Ferguson then established Harry Ferguson Research Ltd and experimented with numerous engineering innovations including a four-wheel-drive system for high performance sports cars. A modified version of this later made it into production in the Jensen FF Interceptor.

Ferguson sold his company to the Canadian agricultural company Massey-Harris in 1953. This was a complex deal that saw Ferguson receive $16 million worth of Massey-Harris shares and the company become Massey-Harris-Ferguson for a period. In 1957 Ferguson resigned from involvement with Massey-Harris-Ferguson and sold his share in the company. In 1958 he was working on the possibility of another tractor development in Britain, but partially as a result of the economic trends of the

■ ABOVE *On the Ferguson TE20 the operator sat astride the gearbox, with feet placed on the footpegs to either side of it.*

■ BELOW *This Ferguson 35, intended to be a successor to the TE20, has a front loader and is towing a muck spreader.*

■ RIGHT
*Ferguson's revised
line of tractors,
designed to
supersede the
TE20s, featured a
much more curved
hood than earlier
models.*

■ BELOW LEFT *A
Ferguson TE20
tractor awaiting
restoration in an
English barn. It
has been painted a
non-standard red
at some time.*

■ BELOW RIGHT
*Harry Ferguson's
trademark was his
surname in italic
script on the top of
the grille surround.*

FERGUSON TE20	
Year	1946
Engine	In-line four cylinder
Power	28hp
Transmission	Four speed
Weight	1 ton 2 cwt/1.12 tonnes

time it came to nothing. Despite this, the Ferguson tractor and the three-point linkage are two of the landmarks in the development of the tractor. The linkage in particular, albeit in a refined form, is the norm throughout the world and still in use on almost every working tractor.

Harry Ferguson then established a consulting engineering company based in Coventry in the West Midlands. This company experimented with numerous engineering innovations including a four-wheel-drive system for high performance Grand Prix cars. The project initially known as the Ferguson Project 99 was eventually developed into a working car and driven by Stirling Moss in 1961.

FIAT

Several of the European nations involved in World War I began to see the value of tractors in increasing farm productivity. In Italy the motor industry undertook experiments with tractors of its own design, and by 1918 the Fiat company had produced a successful tractor known as the 702, while the Pavesi concern introduced an innovative tractor with four-wheel drive and articulated steering.

In 1919 the first mass-produced Fiat tractor, the 702, came off the assembly line. Fiat soon became the major producer of agricultural tractors in Italy and added a crawler to its range in 1932. This was the first tractor that can be considered an earthmoving machine: the 700C was a tractor equipped with a front blade to shift earth and welded devices to load trucks. It was powered by a 30hp four-cylinder engine. Later, but before the outbreak of World War II, Fiat produced the 708C and Model 40.

After the war, in 1950, Fiat launched the Fiat 55, a crawler tractor powered by a 6500cc/396cu in, four-cylinder diesel engine that produced 55hp at 1400rpm. The transmission incorporated a central

■ LEFT *The Fiat 70-90 is one of four tractors in Fiat's Medium 90 Series that ranges from the 55-90 to the 80-90. The first number in the designation refers to the tractor's power output.*

■ BELOW *Fiat Geotech acquired Ford New Holland Inc and merged into one company – New Holland Inc – during 1993.*

FIAT 70-90	
Year	1986
Engine	3613cc/220cu in
Power	70hp
Transmission	n/k
Weight	n/k

■ BELOW LEFT *Like the 90 Series, the 94 models from Fiat are a range of tractors with increasing power outputs. This four-wheel-drive 88-94 model is rated at 88hp.*

pair of bevel gears with final drive by means of spur gears. The crawler tractor had five forward speeds and one reverse. The customer could specify whether they wanted lever or steering-wheel steering. The 6 volt electrical system functioned without a battery and was reliant on a 90 watt dynamo.

In 1962 Fiat created a joint venture with the Turkish company Koa Holding in Ankara, that was known as Türk Traktor. By 1966 Fiat had created its own Tractor and Earthmoving Machinery specialized in the production of small and medium-sized tractors. In 1983 Fiat Trattori entered another joint venture when it combined with the Pakistan Tractor Corporation to pursue a joint venture in Karachi, Pakistan which became known as Al Ghazi Tractors Ltd.

In 1984 Fiat Trattori became Fiatagri, Fiat Group's holding company for the agricultural machinery sector. Things changed again in 1988 when all of Fiat-Allis and Fiatagri's activities were merged to form a new farm and earthmoving machinery company, FiatGeotech. FiatGeotech acquired Benati in 1991, which was later merged with Fiat-Hitachi. Fiat also acquired Ford New Holland Inc and merged it with FiatGeotech. The new company was named N. H. Geotech, but became New Holland Inc in 1993.

Division. This was developed until 1970 when Fiat Macchine e Movimento Terra SpA was founded and carried on the company's activities in the earthmoving sector in its new plant in Lecce, Italy. Shortly afterwards, the new company took over Simit, then the leading Italian manufacturer of hydraulic excavators. In 1974 Fiat Macchine e Movimento Terra entered into a joint venture with the American tractor manufacturer Allis-Chalmers to form Fiat-Allis. In Italy Fiat Trattori SpA was also founded and in 1975 Fiat Trattori became a shareholder of Laverda. In 1977 Fiat Trattori acquired Hesston, as a way of gaining entry into the North American market, and later took over Agrifull, which

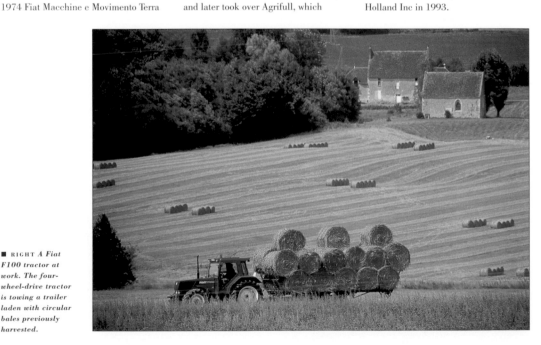

■ RIGHT *A Fiat F100 tractor at work. The four-wheel-drive tractor is towing a trailer laden with circular bales previously harvested.*

FORD

In 1907 the Ford Motor Company built the prototype of what it hoped was to become the world's first mass-produced agricultural tractor. The machine was based around components – including the transmission – from one of Ford's earliest cars. As Henry Ford had grown up on his father's farm, he was aware of the labour-intensive nature of farm work and was keen to develop mechanized ways of doing things. As a result, Ford built his first tractor in 1915, and by 1916 he had a number of working prototypes being evaluated. His aim was to sell to farmers a two-plough tractor for as little as $200, and to do for farmers and farming what the Model T Ford had done for motoring.

With a number of staff, Ford designed what would later become the Fordson Model F. Its secret was its stressed cast-iron frame construction. This frame contained all the moving parts in dustproof and oiltight units, which eliminated many of the weaknesses of early tractors. It had four wheels and was compact. This gave it an unusual appearance at a time when both three-wheeled and massive tractors were the norm.

■ FORDSON MODEL F

The Fordson Model F, Ford's first mass-produced tractor, went into production in 1917. Power came from an in-line four-cylinder gasoline engine that produced 20hp at 1000rpm. A three-speed transmission was fitted with a multiplate clutch that ran in oil and the final drive was by means of a worm gear. The ignition utilized a flywheel-mounted dynamo to supply high tension current to the coil that was positioned on the engine block. The tractor retailed at $750: this was more expensive than Henry Ford had predicted, but the reputation earned by his Model T car ensured that the new tractors sold in large numbers.

Ford's prototypes, seen in action at a tractor trial in Great Britain, were considered a practical proposition and the British government requested that they be put into production immediately to assist with winning the war. Ford was preparing to do exactly that when, in the early summer of 1917, German bombers attacked London in daylight. The Government viewed this new development in the war as a serious one and decided to turn all available

■ LEFT *The Fordson F and N models were the most important tractors in the history of mechanized farming and brought benefits of tractors to a massive number of farmers.*

■ RIGHT *A group of farmers with a Roadless Traction converted E27N Fordson Major tractor.*

FORDSON TRACTOR	
Year	1917
Engine	In-line four cylinder gasoline
Power	20hp
Transmission	Three speed
Weight	1225kg/2700lbs

■ OPPOSITE TOP *A restored example of a 1937 Fordson Model N. Fordson built them in Dagenham, England from 1933.*

■ ABOVE LEFT *The Fordson E27N Major was Ford's first new post-war tractor, and production started in March 1945 at Ford's Dagenham plant in England.*

■ ABOVE *The Fordson Major looked bigger and better than the Fordson Model N. A redesigned clutch, and a spiral bevel and differential drive featured in the new model.*

■ ABOVE *The E27N Major proved popular, and production soared to a peak of 50,000 made in 1948. Many were exported and production continued until 1951.*

■ LEFT *The Fordson Model N assisted Britain's war effort by helping the country grow a much higher percentage of its food requirements than previously.*

■ LEFT *The 1939 Ford Ferguson 9N was innovative because of its hydraulically controlled integral implement hitch. Rubber tyres, electric starter and a PTO were standard.*

■ ABOVE *Harry Ferguson's surname appeared on the Ford 9N as he devised the three-point implement hitch, linked to a hydraulic system.*

■ BELOW *The English Fordson Super Major of the early 1960s, built on the success of the "new" Fordson Major that replaced the E27N Major in 1952.*

■ ABOVE *The Ford 9N sold well. As early as the end of 1940 more than 35,000 had been built and Ferguson's system led other manufacturers to reconsider the hitching of implements.*

industrial production over to the manufacture of fighter aeroplanes in order to combat the German bombers. Ford was asked if he could manufacture his tractors in the United States instead. He agreed and only four months later Fordson F Models were being produced.

While this was only a temporary set-back, the delay and shift in production caused Ford another problem. His plans for his new tractor became public knowledge before the tractors themselves were actually in production, and another company tried to pre-empt his success. In Minneapolis the Ford Tractor Company was set up, using the surname of one of their engineers. The rival tractor produced from this shortlived company was not a great success, but it deprived Henry Ford of the right to use his own name on his tractors. He resorted to the next best thing: Henry

■ BELOW *The Fordson Dexta was a Perkins, three-cylinder, diesel-engined tractor introduced in 1958 to give Fordson dealers a small, low-priced tractor to sell.*

■ LEFT *The Ford 8N was introduced in 1948 after the collapse of the agreement made by Henry Ford and Harry Ferguson.*

■ LEFT *The blue and orange Fordsons were a familiar sight in British fields during the 1950s and 1960s as this one in Hampshire indicates.*

Ford and Son, shortened to Fordson.

The Model F immediately proved popular and US sales increased exponentially from the 35,000 achieved in 1918. By 1922, Fordsons were accounting for approximately 70 per cent of all US tractor sales. By this time the post-war boom in tractor sales had ended. Ford survived by cutting the price of his tractors but his major competitors, notably International Harvester, did the same and the competition became fierce. By 1928 IH had regained the lead in sales and had achieved 47 per cent of the market total.

■ BELOW *Ford celebrated its golden anniversary in 1953 and redesigned its tractors for the occasion. By 1955 the three plough 600 Series was on sale, with a redesigned grille, and red and grey colour scheme.*

■ **CHANGING FACTORIES**
In 1919 production of the Fordson tractor had begun in Cork, Ireland. This was the first tractor to be manufactured simultaneously in the United States and Europe. Production of Fordson tractors in the United States ended in 1928 in the face of major competition from IH and in 1929 all Ford's tractor manufacturing was transferred to Ireland. In 1933 production of Fordson tractors was moved again, this time to Dagenham in England. From Ford's Dagenham factory, Fordsons were

■ RIGHT *The Ford Workmaster series of tractors went on sale in 1959 with a choice of gasoline, diesel or liquid petroleum gas engines. This is a 1960 601 model.*

exported around the world, including back to the USA. Ford produced the All Around row crop tractor in Britain specifically for the USA in 1936. The Fordson was the first foreign tractor tested in Nebraska at the noted Nebraska Tractor Tests, to which it was submitted in both 1937 and 1938. Another Fordson plant was based in the USSR where production was halted in 1932 when the factory switched to making a Soviet copy of the Universal Farmall. Production of Fordson tractors was later restarted in the USA during the 1940s.

The next important innovation – one of the most important in the history of the tractor – was the introduction of the three-point system in the late 1930s. It was to be introduced on Ford's 9N model, having been designed by Harry Ferguson, and is still used on farm tractors today. This ingenious system, combined with a variety of compatible three-point implements, made the tractor a viable replacement for the horse and horse-drawn implements. Ferguson demonstrated the system to Ford in Michigan in autumn 1938 and

■ LEFT *This row crop 961 diesel tractor from 1959 is one of the first Ford tractors to have an American-made diesel engine.*

■ BELOW LEFT *A 601 Ford Work-master, made in 1961, the same year as Ford introduced its largest tractor until then – the five plough 66hp Model 6000.*

through the famous "handshake agreement", by which each man's word was considered sufficient to seal the business partnership, production began. At that time the three-point hitch was known as the Ferguson System and was produced in cooperation with the Ferguson-Sherman Company until 1946.

The Model 9N was first demonstrated in Dearborn, Michigan, on 29 June 1939. This new agricultural concept revolutionized farming. The basic design principles and features incorporated into the 9N are still evident in many of the tractors currently being manufactured. The Ford 9N, the first of the N Series

■ BELOW *The Ford Workmaster models were offered with a choice of engine types. The Model 501 Offset Workmaster increased the versatility of the Ford range.*

■ BELOW *In Britain, Ford tractors, such as this 1962 Ford 5000 diesel, were painted in shades of blue rather than the red and grey favoured in the United States.*

tractors, went on sale complete with the first three-point hitch in 1939. It was developed as a versatile all-purpose tractor for the small farm and was exceedingly popular. The 9N was powered by an in-line four-cylinder 1966cc/120cu in displacement gasoline engine. Many of the engine's internal components, including the pistons, were compatible with parts used in Ford's V8 automobile of the time.

The 9N went through subtle changes during each year of its three-year production run. For example, in 1939 the grille had almost horizontal bars and the steering box, grille, battery box, hood, instrument panel and transmission cover were made of cast aluminium. It also had clip-on radiator and fuel caps, which were changed in 1940 to a hinged

■ BELOW LEFT *The gasoline engine used in the Ford Powermaster models between 1958 and 1961 was this 2820cc/172cu in displacement in-line four-cylinder unit.*

■ BELOW RIGHT *The 861 Powermaster, in its gasoline-engined form.*

FORD 6610 TRACTOR	
Year	1983
Engine	In-line four cylinder diesel
Power	86hp (64 kW)
Transmission	Eight forward, four reverse
Weight	n/k

■ LEFT *A Ford 5000 tractor being used with a specialized implement for the unusual, but highly colourful, task of harvesting tulips.*

type. In 1941 the grille was changed to steel with vertical bars, and many other changes were also made. By the end of 1941 Ford had made so many changes, and had so many more ideas for changes, that the designation of the tractor was changed to the Ford 2N. There were over 99,000 9Ns produced from 1939 to 1942 and almost 200,000 2Ns produced between 1942 and 1947. The 9N's selling price in 1939 was $585, including rubber tyres, an electrical system with a starter, generator and battery, and a power take-off. Headlights and a rear tail-light were optional extras.

The Ford 2N had a relatively short production run. New features

■ LEFT *A Ford TW20, with a large disc harrow, in a Colorado farmyard. The TW20 is one of the high-powered TW range made in American plants.*

■ BELOW LEFT *A Ford 7640 four-wheel-drive tractor. Following the Fiat takeover the Ford name was phased out in favour of New Holland.*

incorporated in its design included an enlarged cooling fan contained within a shroud, a pressurized radiator and, eventually, sealed-beam headlights. Other changes were made here and there as a result of the constraints imposed by the war. For a while, only steel wheels were available because of the rubber shortage caused by Japanese conquests in Asia, and a magneto ignition system was used rather than a battery. When the war ended things reverted to what had been available before. Ford had made 140,000 Model N tractors in England during the war years.

■ LEFT *During the 1980s Ford manufactured its 10 series of tractors at Basildon in Essex, England, one of its eight plants. The 10 series consisted of 11 tractors ranging from 44 to 115hp.*

The Ford 2N eventually evolved into the Ford 8N, a model that officially started its production run in 1947 and was to last until 1952. 1947 was also the year that the much-vaunted handshake agreement on the three-point hitch came to an end. Ford and Ferguson failed to reach an agreement when they tried to renegotiate their deal in the immediate post-war years. Ford declared he would continue using the hitch, but would no longer give Harry Ferguson any money for doing so, nor would he continue to call it the "Ferguson System". As few official business documents existed this resulted in a lawsuit which eventually awarded Harry Ferguson approximately $10 million.

By the time the lengthy lawsuit was finally settled, however, some of Ferguson's patents had expired, enabling Ford to continue production of a hydraulic three-point hitch with only minimal changes. Ferguson then started producing the TE20 and TO20 tractors, in Britain and America respectively, that were similar in appearance to the 8N

and effectively competed with it.

A completely new line of implements was introduced by Ford. Some of the noticeable differences between the 8N and 2N tractors were the change in wheelnuts from six to eight in the rear wheels, a scripted Ford logo on the fenders and sides of the bonnet and

finally, the absence of the Ferguson System logo which was no longer displayed under the Ford oval even though the tractor still used Ferguson's three-point hitch.

Ford's first new post-war tractor made in Dagenham was the Fordson E27N. It was rushed into production at the

■ ABOVE RIGHT *A 1972 diesel-engined Ford 7000 tractor, finished in the distinctive colour scheme that had become standard.*

■ LEFT *A four-wheel-drive Ford 5095 tractor. This model has been additionally protected by the installation of tubular steel bars that extend over the cab for protection during forestry work.*

■ LEFT *The Ford 4110 is one of Ford's English-manufactured, standardized range of 10 Series tractors. A mid-range tractor, its power output is in the region of 50hp.*

a single-plate wet clutch was incorporated. The E27N was powered by an in-line four-cylinder side-valve engine that produced 30hp at 1450rpm. It came in four versions, each with different specifications for brakes, tyres and gear ratios. A variant using a Perkins engine was offered in 1948, and in that year over 50,000 E27Ns were made. Production continued until 1951, with various upgrades and options being made available. These included electrics, hydraulics and a diesel-engined version.

Ford's 50th Anniversary was in 1953 and in that year it introduced the Model NAA Jubilee. This was Ford's first overhead-valve engined tractor; it had a displacement of 2195cc/134cu in and produced 31hp. In 1958 Ford introduced the 600 and 800 Series

request of the British Ministry of Agriculture. The basis of the machine was an upgraded Fordson N engine with a three forward, one reverse gearbox, a conventional clutch and rear axle drive. The Fordson E27N started rolling off the Dagenham production line in March 1945. Ford had made numerous improvements to this tractor over its earlier model. The new tractor featured a spiral bevel and conventional differential instead of a worm drive and

■ BELOW *County tractors, such as this hard-worked forestry tractor, used Ford components in their construction, and equal-sized front and rear wheels.*

■ RIGHT *A Ford tractor, with a seed drill, planting peas. The tractor has dual wheels, front and rear, to reduce soil compaction.*

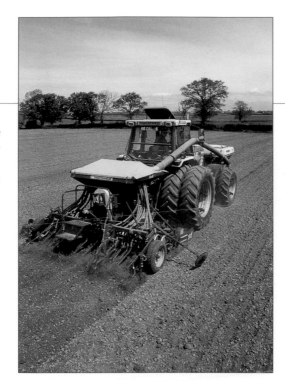

■ OPPOSITE BOTTOM *A four-wheel-drive Ford tractor, with a towed crop spraying unit, at work in Wiltshire, England. The tractor is equipped with weights at the front to improve traction.*

tractors, powered by American-made diesel engines, although gasoline and LPG versions were also offered. These were followed by ranges of tractors known as Powermaster and Workmaster. The Model 8000 was the first Ford tractor to have a 100hp engine, displacing 6571cc/401cu in, while the smaller displacement Model 6000 produced 66hp.

■ CONSOLIDATION

By the 1960s Ford was producing tractors in Brazil, Britain and India as well as in the United States. In 1964 Ford Tractor Operations was moved to Basildon in England. In 1986 the Ford Motor Company acquired New Holland from the Sperry Corporation and merged it with Ford Tractor Operations, naming the new company Ford New Holland.

In Basildon, Ford was producing tractors such as the Model 4610, with an engine of 3300cc/201cu in displacement producing 64hp. This was one of 11 tractors in the 10 Series,

ranging from the Model 2910 (2900cc/177cu in, 44hp) to the Model 8210 (6600cc/403cu in, 115hp). Another of the tractors from the 10 Series was the 4400cc/269cu in displacement, 103hp

Model 7610. Basildon is one of Ford's eight manufacturing plants around the world, and the Company exported to 75 countries.

In 1991 Fiat acquired Ford New Holland Inc and merged it with FiatGeotech, renaming the company N. H. Geotech. Later Versatile Farm Equipment Company became part of Ford New Holland Americas, N. H. Geotech's North American division.

N. H. Geotech changed its name to New Holland Inc in 1993. The Ford name can be used by New Holland Inc only until 2001, by agreement with Fiat.

■ LEFT *The limited slip differential in the front axle of a four-wheel-drive Ford 6810 tractor engages automatically in difficult conditions when it senses wheel spin.*

OTHER MAKES

(Frazier, Gleaner, Hanomag, Hart-Parr,
Hesston, HSCS, Hurlimann)

■ FRAZIER

Frazier is a small specialist company based
outside York in England and is typical of
many companies which produce specialized
farming machines. The IID Agribuggy is
assembled from a number of proprietary
components including axles, suspension
and engines, and is intended as the basis
for tasks such as crop-spraying and
fertilizer spreading. The machines are
purpose-built and offered in both diesel
and petrol forms. The diesel variant is
powered by a four-cylinder Ford engine of
1608cc/98cu in displacement. The
Agribuggy is designed to be adaptable, and
is available in both low ground pressure
and row crop variants.

■ GLEANER

Gleaner has been a manufacturer of
combine harvesters for more than 75 years.
The company currently offers a range of
four rotary combine models as well as the
C-62 conventional combine, all of which
are powered by Cummins liquid-cooled
engines. Gleaner combine harvesters are
built on a one-piece, welded mainframe and
feature a centre-mounted "Comfortech"
cab. Rotary combines are designated as the
R Series, while the C62 is a conventional
combine harvester.

■ LEFT *A pair of
Frazier IID
Agribuggies. The
Agribuggy is
designed as a low
ground pressure
machine for
specialist tasks.*

■ LEFT *An
Agribuggy with low
ground pressure
tyres designed to
minimize soil
compaction.*

■ BOTTOM LEFT
*Gleaner is now part
of the AGCO
corporation. This is
a 1991 model.*

The R42 Gleaner Class 4 combine has
a 6200 litre/170 bushel grain tank and a
450 litre/100 gallon fuel tank, with a 185hp
Cummins engine. The R52 Gleaner Class 5
combine has a standard 8200 litre/225
bushel or optional 8900 litre/245 bushel
grain tank. Its polyurethane fuel tank has a
capacity of 450 litres/100 gallons. A 225hp
Cummins engine is fitted.

The R62 Gleaner Class 6 combine offers
a 260hp in-line six-cylinder engine, and
has as standard an 8200 litre/225 bushel
bin or as an option a 10,900 litre/300
bushel grain tank. The R62 offers
accelerator rolls, chaff spreader, two
distribution augers and a 680 litre/150
gallon fuel tank. The R72 Gleaner is the
only Class 7 combine currently built in
North America. It features a 12,000
litre/330 bushel grain tank and a 300hp in-
line six-cylinder engine. The R72 includes
two distribution augers, accelerator rolls, a
chaff spreader and a 680 litre/150 gallon
fuel tank.

The C-62 conventional combine
harvester is, according to its manufacturers,
built to exceed others in its class. The C-62
has a 10,900 litre/300 bushel grain bin and
a high-capacity, turret unloading system
that delivers grain into trucks and carts at a
rate of 80 litres/2.2 bushels per second.
The C62 is constructed around an all-
welded frame using heavy-duty final drives
and is designed with even weight
distribution and the strength needed for
large loads. Under it all is fitted a 260hp
Cummins diesel engine.

Gleaner is part of the AGCO Corporation
– indeed AGCO is a acronym for the Allis-
Gleaner Corporation.

■ LEFT *As can
be seen from
this 1967
Gleaner CR
combine,
provision for the
operator has
progressed
considerably in
only thirty
years. Air
conditioned,
dust-proofed
cabs are now
standard.*

■ HANOMAG

The German company Hanomag of Hanover was offering a massive six-furrow motor plough at the outbreak of World War I. It was, like other German machines of the time, intended for the plains of Germany. In the years after the war it offered a larger version with an eight-furrow plough and an 80hp four-cylinder gasoline engine. By the 1930s Hanomag was thriving, partially as a result of exports of both its crawler and wheeled machines. In 1930 it offered the R38 and R50 wheeled models and the K50 crawler. All were diesel-powered and featured a power take-off.

Hanomag contributed to the German war effort and its factories suffered extensive damage. The company resumed production of tractors in the late 1940s and offered the four-cylinder diesel R25, finished in red.

A Hanomag twin-cylinder diesel engine was later incorporated in the European versions of the Massey-Harris Pony, built in France. Hanomag continued to offer its R-range of tractors, including the small R12 and R24 Models alongside larger R45 and R55 Models, through the 1960s.

A change of ownership of the company in 1971 resulted in the cessation of all tractor manufacture.

■ LEFT *Hanomag had success with export sales of both wheeled and crawler tractors during the 1930s.*

■ ABOVE *A four-wheel-drive Hanomag 35D hydraulic loader, working on corn silage in England.*

OTHER MAKES

HART-PARR

Charles Hart and Charles Parr were engineering students together at the University of Wisconsin and graduated in 1896. They formed a company in Madison, Wisconsin to build stationary engines. These were unusual in that they used oil rather than water for cooling, which was an asset in areas that suffered harsh winters. As oil freezes at a considerably lower temperature than water, damage to engines caused by freezing coolant could thereby be avoided. Hart and Parr moved to Charles City, Iowa in 1901 and made their first tractor in 1902. The Model 18–30 followed it in 1903. This had a distinctive rectangular cooling tower which then became a distinguishing feature of all Hart-Parr tractors for the next 15 years. The cooling system circulated the oil around vertical tubes within the tower and air flow through it was maintained by directing the exhaust gases into the tower. The engine was rated at 30hp and was of a two-cylinder horizontal design with a large displacement that operated at around 300rpm. The 17–30 was a further development, and this was followed by numerous others, including the 12–27 Oil King.

Hart-Parr redesigned its machinery for

■ LEFT *Hart-Parr became the Oliver Farm Equipment Corporation of Chicago in a merger of 1929.*

■ BELOW LEFT *Early Hart-Parr tractors were characterized by the rectangular cooling tower.*

the boom after World War I. The 12–25 was one of the new models and featured a horizontal twin-cylinder engine. Later these tractors were offered with an engine-driven power take-off, but the full import of this advance was not realized until later. Oliver acquired Hart-Parr in 1929.

HESSTON

In 1947 the Hesston company was founded in Kansas, United States. It became a respected manufacturer of hay and forage machinery, recognized for its innovative products and with industrial and marketing offshoots in Europe. In 1977 Fiat Trattori took over Hesston in order to gain entry

into the North American agricultural machinery market. In 1988 all of Fiat-Allis and Fiatagri's activities were merged to form a new company, FiatGeotech, Fiat's group farm and earthmoving machinery sector. As part of this restructuring Hesston and Braud joined forces in a new company, Hesston-Braud, based in Coex, France.

HSCS

Hofherr, Schrantz, Clayton and Shuttleworth was formed in Hungary after Clayton and Shuttleworth's withdrawal from the steam traction engine market in that country. Initially the company's headquarters was in Kispest but it later moved to Budapest. The company started making gasoline engines in 1919, leading to the production of its first tractor in 1923. This used a single-cylinder gasoline engine for its motive power and was assembled around a steel frame. Production versions of the HSCS tractor used single semi-diesel engines, a configuration that was popular in much of Europe but not in the UK nor the United States. The perceived advantages of the semi-diesel engine are that it is mechanically simple and will run on almost any type of fuel, including waste oil. The HSCS engine was rated at 14hp and was intended for ploughing and as a source of stationary power.

The company persevered with semi-diesels throughout the production of numerous wheeled and crawler tractors. An HSCS tractor competed in the 1930 World Tractor Trials held in Britain.

In 1951, under the auspices of the communist regime, the company name was changed to Red Star Tractor. From 1960 onwards the products were sold under the

DUTRA brand name – an amalgamation of the words "Dumper" and "Tractor", representing the company's product range. Tractors were exported to other eastern bloc countries and beyond. Later the company produced RABA-Steiger tractors under licence from Steiger.

■ HURLIMANN

Hurlimann tractors reflect the farming conditions peculiar to Switzerland, a small mountainous country. It has little room suited to the production of arable crops and Hans Hurlimann started in business to build tractors suited to the country. His first machine used a single cylinder gasoline engine, and was fitted with a power bar grass mower.

The first tractors were considered to be old fashioned but development work and upgrades through the 1930s led to a new model introduced in 1939. This was fitted with a direct injection, four-cylinder diesel

■ TOP RIGHT A Hungarian-manufactured HSCS tractor from the 1940s. HSCS stood for Hofherr Schrantz Clayton and Shuttleworth.

■ RIGHT A Hurlimann S200 tractor manufactured during the 1970s. Hurlimann was one of several Swiss tractor makers at the time.

engine and led to Hurlimann exporting tractors, and selling them to the Swiss military as gun tractors. These tractors proved popular, and another new model – the D-100 – was introduced in 1945.

The D-100 was equipped with a PTO, two speed belt pulley and a differential lock. It also featured both hand and foot throttles and a five speed transmission. The tractor produced 45hp at 1600rpm, and had a low centre of gravity achieved by the use of 56cm/22in diameter rear wheels. Hurlimann continued exporting tractors and later became part of the Italian Same company.

■ RIGHT Hurlimann's D-100 was acknowledged as a well-engineered tractor retaining a low centre of gravity through the fitment of smaller than normal diameter rear wheels.

■ ABOVE Hurlimann used a diesel engine in its 1930s tractors, supplied to the Swiss Army as gun tractors.

INTERNATIONAL HARVESTER

■ BELOW *The Farmall series became popular during the 1930s, when pneumatic tyres were still only available as an extra-cost option. The range included the F-12, F-20 and F-30 models.*

The International Harvester Corporation was formed in 1902 through the merger of two small tractor makers, McCormick and Deering.

The history of International Harvester really began in 1831, when Cyrus McCormick invented a reaper which quickly became known as the "Cornbinder". The fledgling IH at first marketed two ranges of tractors, the Mogul and Titan models. The former was sold by McCormick dealers and the latter by Deering dealers. The first IH tractors appeared in 1906 when the Type A gasoline tractor was marketed with a choice of 12, 15 and 20hp engines. The Type B soon followed and lasted until 1916. IH was noted for its production of the giant 45hp Mogul tractor during the second decade of the 20th century. It followed this in 1919 with the Titan, a 22hp machine. International Harvester also produced light trucks alongside its tractors.

During World War I many American tractors were exported to Great Britain and International Harvester Corporation marketed the models from its range that were considered most suited to British conditions. These were the Titan 10–20 and the Mogul 8–16.

■ TITAN 10–20

The International Harvester Titan 10–20 was built in the Milwaukee, Wisconsin factory and was the smallest and most popular model in the Titan range. Mogul tractors were built in parallel in the Chicago, Illinois factory. Production of the 10–20 started in 1914 and lasted for

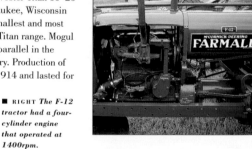

■ RIGHT *The F-12 tractor had a four-cylinder engine that operated at 1400rpm.*

■ LEFT *The Farmall F-12 was introduced in 1932. It was a row crop tractor, rated as a one to two plough tractor. One benefit was its infinitely adjustable rear hubs.*

FARMALL F-20	
Year	1932
Engine	Four cylinder
Power	16.12 drawbar and 24.13 belt hp
Transmission	Four speed
Weight	n/k

■ RIGHT *The Farmall M was introduced in 1939 as a row crop tractor styled by Raymond Loewy. It was to become one of the classic American tractors of all time.*

■ BELOW LEFT *The switch from grey to red paint was made in 1936 but rubber tyres were available prior to this as this tricycle row crop model suggests.*

■ BELOW MIDDLE *Pneumatic tyres were offered for both the front and rear of the Farmall row crop models as seen on this tractor at a South Dakota vintage rally.*

■ BELOW RIGHT *Dwayne Mathies on the Farmall row crop tractor bought new by his family for their South Dakota, USA farm. Four generations of Mathies have now sat astride it.*

a decade because the simplicity of the design ensured a reputation for reliability. The 10–20 was powered by a paraffin-fuelled, twin-cylinder engine of large displacement that achieved 20hp at only 575rpm. The engine was cooled by water contained in a cylindrical 180 litre/40 gallon tank positioned over the front wheels. The Titan 10–10 was assembled on a steel girder frame. It was chain driven and had a two-speed transmission. More than 78,000 were made and it was one of several models of tractor that were to carry the company into the 1920s. Others produced in that decade included the 8–16, the 15–30 and the Farmall Regular.

■ IH 8–16 TRACTOR

The International Harvester 8–16 was produced in the United States during World War I and proved popular. It had a distinctive appearance, with a sloping hood over the engine and radiator. Production commenced in 1917 and lasted until 1922. The design, although

inspired by the IH truck line, was old-fashioned at the time of its introduction as it was based on a separate frame and featured chain and sprocket final drive. However, the availability of a power take-off as an optional extra gave the 8–16 an advantage over its competitors

as the tractor could be used to drive other machinery. While IH could not claim to have invented the PTO (it had been used on a British Scott tractor in 1904) it was the first company to have commercial success with the innovation. IH made it a standard fitting on its

■ LEFT *The Farmall F-14 replaced the F-12 in 1938. It was a slight upgrade of the earlier model with an engine that operated at 1650rpm and made 14.84 drawbar and 17.44 belt hp at Nebraska.*

■ RIGHT *It was industrial designer Raymond Loewy who gave the Farmall tractors the horizontal barred grille and rounded radiator grille shell during the 1930s.*

■ BELOW *Diesel engines were another innovation introduced to the Farmall range during the 1930s.*

McCormick-Deering 15-30 tractor introduced in 1921.

As the initial post-war wave of prosperity subsided in the early 1920s. Ford cut its prices to keep sales up and, faced with this competition, IH offered a plough at no extra cost with each tractor it sold. This had the effect of shifting all IH stock, allowing the company to introduce the 15–30 and 10–20 models in 1921 and 1923 respectively. These machines were to give Ford competition in a way that that company had not experienced before. The new IH models were constructed in a similar way to the Fordson, around a stressed cast frame,

but incorporated a few details that gave them the edge on the Fordson. These included a magneto ignition, a redesigned clutch and a built-in PTO, setting a new standard for tractors.

■ **MCCORMICK-DEERING**

The International Harvester 10–20 of 1923 was said to offer "sturdy reliability" and power, and it went on to become an outstanding success in the United States where it was generally known as the McCormick-Deering 10–20. It remained in production until 1942, by which time 216,000 machines

had been sold. The styling of the 10–20 owed a lot to the larger 15–30: both models were powered by an in-line four-cylinder petrol and paraffin engine with overhead valves that were designed for long usage with replaceable cylinder liners. A crawler version of the 10-20 was unveiled in 1928 and was the first crawler produced by International Harvester; known as the TracTracTor, it was to become the T-20 in 1931.

In 1924 the company progressed further with the introduction of the Farmall, the first proper row crop tractor. It could be used for ploughing but could also turn its capabilities to cultivation. It

■ ABOVE *The Farmall M was offered on pneumatic tyres as standard at the time of its introduction, although steel wheels were a lower cost option. An electric starter and lights were also optional extras.*

■ LEFT *A mix of famous brands as a red Farmall row crop ploughs using a two-furrow plough in the familiar yellow and green colour scheme that shows it was made by John Deere.*

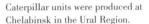

was suitable for use along rows of cotton, corn and other crops. It was refined and redesigned for the 1930s, when the Farmall Regular became one of a range of three models as the F-20, with the F-12 and F-30. These machines were similar but had different capacities.

In 1929 the 15–30 had become the 22–36 and was subsequently replaced by the W-30 in 1934. The 10–20 had a long production run, being made until 1939. IH dropped its hitherto traditional grey paint scheme during the 1930s and replaced it with red. The effect of this was twofold: first, it allowed the tractors to be more visible to other motorists as they became more widely used on public roads; secondly they were more noticeable to potential buyers. In the USSR at Kharkov and Stalingrad the International Harvester 15-30 went into production as the SKhTZ 15-30 and engines based on

■ ABOVE LEFT *Later International Harvesters were fitted with additional equipment such as the front loader on this Farmall model.*

■ ABOVE RIGHT *A restored example of the Farmall Super FC-D tractor. It retains the adjustable rear wheel spacing and the streamlined Raymond Loewy design.*

■ BELOW *This Farmall M is the tricycle row crop type and is fitted with a hydraulic front loader.*

Caterpillar units were produced at Chelabinsk in the Ural Region.

The first IH wheeled, diesel-powered tractor appeared in 1934, designated the WD-40. It was powered by a four-cylinder engine and the numerical suffix referred to its power, in the region of 44bhp. The engine was slightly unorthodox in that it was started on petrol and once warm switched to diesel through the closure of a valve.

■ THE W-MODELS

The International Harvester W6 was announced in 1940 as part of a range of new tractors. The range also included the W4 and W9 models and all were powered by an in-line four-cylinder engine that produced 36.6hp when running on gasoline and slightly less on paraffin. A diesel version was designated the WD6.

■ LEFT *The Farmall A was also new in 1939, it was a small machine with adjustable tread front wheels and an engine and transmission offset to the left of the tractor.*

■ RIGHT *Clearly visible on this standard tractor is the steering arrangement to the front axle and the infinitely adjustable rear track by means of the splined hubs.*

■ RIGHT *The International 584 tractor, seen with a muck spreader on an English winter's day.*

■ BELOW *The International 955 was a four-wheel-drive model, made before Tenneco Inc merged Case and International Harvester.*

In the late 1930s the industrial designer Raymond Loewy redesigned IH's trademark before moving on to deal with the appearance of the company's range of tractors. It was he who gave them their rounded radiator grille with horizontal slots. The new styling initially appeared on the crawler tractors but soon after the Farmall M models were restyled in the same way.

During World War II IH manufactured a range of machinery for the war effort, including half-track vehicles for the allied armies. The company produced more than 13,000 International M-5

■ RIGHT *International Harvesters from different decades. International Harvester suffered during the United States farm crisis of the early 1980s.*

■ BELOW *Hay bales being loaded by hand on to a farm trailer on a Yorkshire Dales farm in England.*

half-tracks at its Springfield plant. It also made a number of "essential use" pick-ups for civilians who required transport in order to assist the war effort.

■ **OVERSEAS OPERATION**
The W6 was improved in the first years of the 1950s, when the model was redesignated as the Super W6 and Super M, from International Harvester and Farmall respectively. The bore was increased slightly to give the tractors an extra 10hp. The more established American tractor manufacturers quickly added new models to their ranges in the immediate post-war years and IH was no exception. The company replaced the Model A with the Super A, which gained a hydraulic rear-lift attachment as hydraulics began to be more widely used.

In the post-war years IH was one of the three large American tractor manufacturers to establish factories in Britain. It opened a factory in Doncaster,

■ RIGHT
International Harvester still manufacture harvesting machinery including combine harvesters such as these.

■ FAR RIGHT TOP
The Farmall Cub was the smallest tractor in the range, built throughout the years between 1949 and 1979.

■ FAR RIGHT
MIDDLE *A 1965 International Cub.*

■ BOTTOM RIGHT
A restored example of a Farmall Model C. This model replaced the earlier Model B when introduced with the Farmall Cub in 1947.

South Yorkshire, while Allis-Chalmers opted for Hampshire and Massey-Harris for Manchester, although it moved to Kilmarnock, Scotland in 1949. IH was the only company to have noteworthy commercial success, assembling the Farmall M for the British market.

■ **DIESEL TECHNOLOGY**

In 1959 the American tractor manufacturers adopted industry standards for the increasingly popular three-point hitches to make farm implements more versatile by increasing their interchangeability between makes. To meet this standard, IH offered new tractors for 1960 – the 404 and 504 models – that offered the first American-designed, draught-sensing three-point hitch. The 504 also came with power steering while both models featured dry air cleaners and a means of cooling the hydraulic fluid. The 1960s saw increasing refinements made to the diesel engine as turbochargers and intercoolers were

developed. IH embraced the new technology and developed better transmissions and four-wheel-drive systems as farming became more mechanized. By the 1970s the Farmall 966 was a 100hp machine with 16 forward and two reverse gears and a 6784cc/414cu in displacement engine.

The economic crisis of the early 1980s was to have far-reaching consequences within the American agricultural industry. International Harvester was a casualty of the recession. In the 1980 financial year the company's losses exceeded $3,980 million and the following year they were similarly high. In 1982 the situation worsened as losses totalled more than $1.6 billion. Despite this catastrophe the losses were reduced to $485 million for 1983, but IH could not survive. In 1984 Tenneco Inc, which already controlled Case, bought IH's agricultural products division and formed Case IH.

JCB

■ BELOW *A JCB 1115 Fastrac, spreading granular fertilizer from an Amazone N1209 spreader. The 1115 produces 115hp and can haul as much as a 24 tonne gross train weight.*

The British plant manufacturer JCB currently produces a comprehensive range of machines including the famous "digger", with a front loader and backhoe. JCB also produces wheeled and tracked excavators. It is the company's range of crawler tractors, the Fastracs, that are wholly designed for agricultural applications.

■ JCB FASTRAC

The JCB Fastrac is a modern high speed tractor. The Fastrac features a unique all-round suspension system and a spacious ROPS (rollover protective structure) and FOPS (falling objects protective structure) cab with air-conditioning and passenger seat as standard. It has four equal-sized wheels. The Fastrac has a three-point implement mounting position and the optional JCB Quadtronic four-wheel steering system is available on the 2115, 2125 and 2135 Fastrac models. This automatically switches between two-wheel and four-wheel steering for quicker headland turns. Power comes from turbo diesel engines that produce 115–170hp. The

diesel Perkins 1000 Series high torque engine is quiet and fuel-efficient. All models are turbocharged: the 2135 has a waste guard turbo while the 2150 has a waste guard and intercooler. This is coupled to a three-speed Powershift transmission and an electronic transmission controller which has been designed to ensure smooth changes under load. The suspension and chassis use equally advanced technology, including a three-link front suspension that allows the tyres to tuck in against the chassis for a tight turning circle.

JCB FASTRAC 2150	
Year	1998
Engine	Perkins 1000 Series turbo diesel
Power	133 PTO hp, 150hp
Transmission	54 forward, 18 reverse
Weight	6365kg/14,032lbs

■ LEFT *The JCB Fastrac is designed to be versatile. It operates both at the slow speeds required in fields, and at up to 72kph (45mph) on roads. Many of the machine's functions are controlled by computer.*

■ RIGHT *The JCB Fastrac, introduced in 1991, features self-levelling suspension and a turbo diesel engine. Different models in the range had different outputs ranging from 115 to 170hp.*

Self-levelling on the rear suspension compensates for the additional weight of implements and self-levelling from side to side assists boom stability which is useful when working on hillsides. Optional adjustable wheel-slip control, working in conjunction with a radar sensor that measures true ground speed, helps reduce tyre wear and soil smearing. Air over hydraulic disc brakes are fitted on all four wheels and the external disc brakes allow cooling.

■ BELOW *A JCB Fastrac 150, working with a Claas Quadrant 1200 square baler. Unusually for a tractor, the Fastrac cab has room to accommodate a passenger, and a seat has been fitted for them.*

■ TRANSMISSION

Inside the cab, the JCB electrical monitoring system (EMS) provides a performance assessment of the numerous machine functions on the dashboard. It includes the engine rpm, PTO rpm, selected Powershift ratio and a full range of warning indicators, such as one indicating whether the front or rear PTO is selected.

The axle drive shafts have double seals on the bearing cups to retain more grease for longer life. Improved axle drive shafts and cross serrated drive shaft location is designed to ensure durability and longer component life. The heavy-duty front axles feature a solid bearing spacer between the pinion bearing for improved durability. Soft engage differential-lock, fitted as standard to the rear axle, can be selected when wheels are spinning. It engages smoothly to protect the drive train and then automatically disengages when four-wheel steering is operated or when the "differential-lock cut-out" is selected.

JOHN DEERE

■ BELOW *Soon after its introduction, the John Deere GP tractor was offered in a variety of configurations. These included the tricycle row crop, and its derivatives the Models A and B.*

The history of the massive John Deere company starts in 1837. In that year John Deere, a 33-year-old pioneer blacksmith from Vermont, designed and made a "self-polishing" steel plough in his small blacksmith's shop in Grand Detour, Illinois. He made it from the steel of a broken saw blade and found that the plough was capable of slicing through the thick, sticky prairie soil efficiently without becoming stuck or forcing itself out of the ground. As it cut the furrow it became polished and this ensured that the soil would not stick. It was a major breakthrough in farming technology and became the first commercially successful steel plough in America. The plough was fundamental in opening the American Midwest to agriculture and ensuring high levels of crop production.

■ EXPANSION

With a succession of partners, John Deere made an increasing number of ploughs each year. The supply of broken saw blades was of course limited, so at first Deere had steel shipped from England. In 1846 the first plough steel ever rolled in the United States was made to order for John Deere in Pittsburgh. In 1848 Deere moved his

■ RIGHT *The John Deere GP model: the designation GP stood for General Purpose. It was introduced in 1928 and was designed as a three-row cultivating tractor.*

■ BELOW *A restored John Deere GP Model A, with a two-furrow plough. The Model A was introduced in 1934 and most were like this tricycle row crop version.*

JOHN DEERE MODEL A	
Year	1934
Engine	Two cylinder, 5047cc/308cu in
Power	18.72 drawbar hp, 24.71 belt hp
Transmission	Two speed
Weight	1840kg/4059lbs

operation to Moline, Illinois, to make use of the Mississippi River to power his factory's machinery and for distribution of his products. By 1852 Deere, Tate and Gould were making approximately 4000 ploughs per year. This partnership did not last long – in fact Tate later became a competitor – and by 1856 John Deere's son Charles was working at

■ ABOVE *Steel lugged wheels gave traction while in the field, but meant the tractor was not permitted to run on roads.*

■ LEFT *The advent of the pneumatic agricultural tyre can be considered a major step on the road to the modern complex tractor.*

the company. In 1868 it was incorporated as Deere & Company.

Charles Deere went on to expand the company established by his father. He was reputed to be an outstanding businessman, and established marketing centres, called branch houses, to serve his network of independent retail dealers. During the 1880s John Deere was able to offer financing to retail customers for its agricultural products. By the time of Charles Deere's death in 1907, the company was making a wide

■ RIGHT *For all the technological advances that have been made within tractor technology, some things have changed remarkably little. In John Deere's case the brand name and colour scheme of the tractors have remained constant.*

■ LEFT *The John Deere Model B was introduced in 1935. It was smaller than the Model A and rated at 11.84 drawbar and 16.01 belt hp in the Nebraska Tests.*

■ BELOW LEFT *Industrial designer, Henry Dreyfuss, redesigned the Model A and B tractors to give them aesthetically pleasing lines, and to keep up with the competition.*

■ BELOW RIGHT *The Model A and B GP tractors both featured infinitely adjustable rear wheel tread.*

■ BOTTOM *In excess of 322,200 John Deere Model B tractors were made between 1935 and 1952.*

range of steel ploughs, cultivators, corn and cotton planters, and other farming implements.

■ **ACQUISITION**

In 1911, under Deere & Company's third president, William Butterworth, six farm equipment companies were acquired and incorporated into the Deere organization, going a long way to establishing the company as a manufacturer of a complete range of farm equipment. In 1918, the company purchased the Waterloo Gasoline Engine Company in Waterloo, Iowa, and this put it in the tractor business. Tractors, of course, went on to become one of the most important parts of the John Deere business and meant that the modern era of the John Deere Company had begun.

■ RIGHT *A*
Dreyfuss-styled,
John Deere tricycle
row crop tractor,
with a two row
planter. The
success of the
design ensured a
long production
run for this tractor.

■ RIGHT *New for*
1937 was the John
Deere Model G,
capable of pulling
a three furrow
plough. The Model
G produced 20.7
drawbar and 31.44
belt hp.

■ RIGHT *A 1935*
John Deere Model
A, with the more
utilitarian pre-
Dreyfuss styling.
Numerous variants
of the Model A
were produced,
including orchard
models.

At the time of the acquisition, the
Waterloo Gasoline Traction Engine
Company was making its Model N
tractor and under John Deere's
supervision this model was kept in
production until 1924. It was the subject
of the first ever Nebraska Tractor Test in
1920. The Model N was rated
as a 12–25 model when the tests
confirmed outputs of 12.1 drawbar
and 25.51 belt hp.

■ **JOHN DEERE MODEL D**
During the 1920s the company
introduced its two-cylinder Model D
tractor. Many other tractor-makers were
offering four-cylinder machines at the
time but Deere's engineers, aware that
the post-war boom in tractor sales was
over, considered the economics of both
manufacture and maintenance and
designed the two-cylinder engine.
History showed that their decision was
correct as the Model D was a
particularly successful machine. It was
Deere's interpretation of the cast frame
tractor, powered by a two-cylinder

■ LEFT *The provision of a belt drive pulley on tractors was originally as important as the fitment of a drawbar, as it enabled the farmer to drive a variety of equipment.*

achieved 38–42hp in the same tests. The distinctive exhaust note made by these two-cylinder machines earned them the nickname of "Johnny Poppers".

■ **JOHN DEERE GP**

John Deere brought out a row crop tractor in 1928 known as the GP. In the same year, Charles Deere Wiman, a great-grandson of John Deere, took over direction of the company. During the period when modern agriculture was developing, his strong emphasis on engineering and product development resulted in rapid growth. The GP designation indicated General Purpose. It was designed as a three-row row crop machine and was the first John Deere tractor with a power lift for raising attached implements. Sufficient crop clearance was achieved by having a curved front axle and step-down gearing

kerosene/paraffin engine and fitted with a two forward and one reverse speed gearbox. From this basic machine a production run of sequentially upgraded tractors continued until 1953, by which time more than 160,000 had been made. The scale of upgrades can be gauged from the fact that the 1924 model achieved a rating of 22–30hp when tested in Nebraska while the 1953 model

JOHN DEERE 4010 TRACTOR	
Year	1959
Engine	In-line six cylinder
Power	73.65 drawbar hp
Transmission	Eight speed
Weight	3175kg/7000lbs

■ FAR RIGHT *The power take-off (PTO) shaft and linkage for hitching up implements are clearly visible on the rear of this restored row crop John Deere.*

■ RIGHT *A restored example of a 1931 John Deere GP. The engine flywheel is clearly visible on this side, and the belt pulley is on the other.*

to the rear wheels. Unfortunately it did not prove as successful as had been hoped, so John Deere's engineers went back to the drawing board and produced the GPWT. The WT part of the designation indicated Wide Tread and the machine was of a tricycle configuration. In subsequent years a number of variants of this model were produced, including models for orchard use and potato farming – the GPO and GP-P models.

■ BELOW *The row crop tricycle tractor was one of the first specialist designs of tractor to be developed, and it found appreciative customers in a short space of time.*

Through the Great Depression, and despite financial losses in the early 1930s, Deere elected to carry debtor farmers as long as was necessary. The result was a loyalty among the primary customer base that extends across three generations to the present day. Despite the setbacks of the Depression, the company achieved $100 million in gross sales for the first time in its history in 1937, the year of its centennial celebration.

■ **JOHN DEERE MODEL A**

The Model A was a John Deere machine produced between 1934 and 1952. It was a tricycle row crop tractor that incorporated numerous innovations. The

■ ABOVE *Although John Deere came late to the tractor manufacturing business, after its acquisition of Waterloo Boy, the company wasted no time in catching up and developing new models.*

■ BELOW *The size and scale of prairie farming in the United States led to the development of larger tractors with much more powerful engines.*

wheel track was adjustable through the use of splined hubs and the transmission was contained in a single-piece casting. The first Model A was rated at 18 drawbar and 24 belt hp but this output was subsequently increased. By the time production of the Model A was halted in 1952 over 328,000 had been made. Another tractor to have a long and successful production run was John Deere's Model B, manufactured between 1935 and 1952. It was smaller than the A and rated at 11 drawbar and 16 belt hp. It was later produced in numerous forms including the model BO and the crawler-track equipped version of the 1940s. The MC model made later was purpose-built as a crawler tractor.

■ ECONOMIC RECOVERY

By 1937 the American economy was well on the way to recovery and in 1938 the company unveiled a range of tractors

■ ABOVE *A row crop 630. The 30 Series was the last range of two-cylinder John Deere-engined tractors.*

■ LEFT *The new diesel-powered Model R was Deere's most powerful tractor when introduced in 1949.*

■ LEFT *The two tone 20 Series made its debut in 1956, and featured a yellow stripe on the sides of the hood and radiator shell. The engines of tractors such as the 620 had redesigned cylinder heads to increase their power.*

■ RIGHT *A John Deere tractor in preservation. It is easy to understand the high regard in which these iron beasts of burden are held after years of reliable service.*

■ BOTTOM *A restored John Deere tractor at a summer vintage machinery rally in South Dakota, United States.*

■ BELOW *The Model G Series was in production between 1942 and 1953.*

supplied as the standard fitment, although the rubber shortages caused by World War II caused the maker to return to steel wheels.

■ **POST-WAR YEARS**

John Deere's factories produced a wide range of war-related products, ranging from tank transmissions to mobile laundry units. Throughout this period John Deere nonetheless maintained its emphasis on product design, and developed a strong position for the post-war market through the efforts of Messrs Wiman and its wartime president, Burton Peek. Before Wiman's death in 1955, the company was firmly established as one of the nation's 100 largest manufacturing businesses. Through the first post-war decade, from 1946 to 1954, many new products and innovations were introduced, including the company's first self-propelled

that had been redesigned by the industrial designer, Henry Dreyfuss. The company's management was conscious that the John Deere line had changed little between 1923 and 1937, while many of its competitors were moving towards stylized tractors and taking their design cues from the automobile makers of the time. The Models A and B were the first restyled tractors, although mechanically the Model B was similar to the one originally introduced in 1935. They were followed by the similarly styled D and H Models in 1939 and the Model G in 1942. The Model H was a lightweight two-row tricycle tractor and in excess of 60,000 were made. The Model G was a three-plough tractor rated at 20–31hp. It was the most powerful tractor in John Deere's line-up at the time. By the time of its manufacture pneumatic tyres were

■ BELOW *John Deere unveiled its new generation of power tractors in 1959. From then on, the size and power output of agricultural tractors continued to increase.*

■ BELOW *The 5010 tractor was a large diesel-powered machine, more than capable of pulling a forage harvester and drawbar trailer, as seen here.*

combine harvester, cotton picker and combine corn head. The latter was one of John Deere's most successful harvesting innovations. The company also made electric starting and lights standard on its post-war tractors.

■ LEFT *During the 1960s John Deere developed products that were aimed at specialist markets, such as this ride-on lawn mower.*

■ BELOW *A John Deere No 45. The operator is in the open, exposed to all the dust and noise of harvesting.*

■ OPPOSITE BELOW *A John Deere Model 55-H sidehill combine in Wenatchee, Washington, USA during 1954.*

■ **JOHN DEERE MODEL M**
All the more established American tractor manufacturers quickly added new models to their ranges in the immediate post-war years. John Deere was no exception and replaced the Models H, LA and L with the Model M in 1947. This was followed by two derivatives, the Models MC and MT, a crawler and tricycle, in 1949. The Model M was made between 1947 and 1952 while the MT was made between 1949 and 1952. Production of both models totalled more than 70,000. The MC was John Deere's first designed and constructed crawler machine and in the Nebraska Tractor Tests it achieved a rating of 18–22hp. A variety of track widths was made available to customers and more than 6,000 tractors had been made by 1952. The MC and the industrial variant of the Model M, the MI, went on to become the basis of John Deere's Industrial Equipment Division.

John Deere's first diesel tractor was produced in 1949 and designated the Model R before the company switched to

■ LEFT *The modern combine harvester contrasts with the earlier machine, not least because of the increased level of comfort afforded to the operator, which inevitably has a positive effect on productivity.*

followed in sequence through the 1950s and 60s. The 50 and 60 Series, for example, replaced the Models B and A respectively in 1952 while the 80 Series replaced the Model R.

In 1956 the John Deere 20 Series tractors were announced as a range of six different machines designated sequentially from 320 to 820. Of these, the 820 was the largest and was the only diesel model. Despite this it had a horizontal twin-cylinder engine – John Deere's established configuration. The 820, in many ways an upgraded Model R tractor, produced 64.3hp at 1125rpm, meaning that it was the most powerful machine John Deere had built up until that time. The engine displaced 7726 cc/471.5cu in through a bore and stroke of 15.5 × 20cm/6.125 × 8in. Starting was by means of a small-capacity V4 petrol engine. The 820 was fitted with a hydraulic lift as standard although PTO

a numerical designation for its tractors. The Model R was the replacement for the Model D and was based on engineering and design that had been started during the war years. It was a powerful machine that gave 45.7 drawbar and 51 brake hp in the Nebraska Tests. The large displacement diesel that powered the Model R was started by means of an electric start, two-cylinder gasoline engine. More than 21,000 Model Rs were built between its introduction in 1949 and 1954 when production ceased.

■ **JOHN DEERE 20 SERIES**
John Deere switched to a system of numerical designations for its tractors in 1952 and the machines that followed were the 20 Series of the mid-1950s, the 30 Series introduced in 1958 and the 40, 50 , 60, 70 and 80 Series that

■ RIGHT *This John Deere tractor has been fitted with a hydraulically operated bale and silage grapple, one of six different units that can be fitted on John Deere's hydraulic front loader.*

was an optional extra. The 820 weighed in excess of 4 tons and was, according to its manufacturer, capable of pulling six 35cm/14in furrows. This tractor had a short production run that ended in 1958, but it was one of the first in the trend towards ever larger and more powerful tractors.

■ WORLDWIDE MARKETING

In the mid-1950s manufacturing and marketing operations had been expanded into both Mexico and Germany, marking the beginning of the company's growth into a major multinational corporation. In 1958 Deere's Industrial Equipment Division was officially established, suggesting future diversification. In fact, Deere had

■ LEFT *John Deere's first four-wheel-drive tractor was added to the company's range in 1959. This is a later 2130 model.*

■ BELOW *The John Deere Pro-Series offers up to 24 row spacing configurations.*

■ RIGHT *The 1956 John Deere 20 series comprised of six tractors ranging from the 320 to the 820.*

■ BELOW *The 20 range featured a two-tone colour scheme, a revised layout of the controls, and a sprung seat to make operation of the tractor easier for the driver.*

JOHN DEERE 9976 PRO-SERIES COTTON PICKER	
Year	1997
Engine	Six-cylinder 497cu in (8. litre) turbocharged diesel
Power	300hp (224kW)
Transmission	Three speed
Weight	39,630 lbs (15,602 kg) six row

■ BELOW *Contemporary John Deere loaders have a lift height of up to 3.5m (11ft 5in) and a reach of up to 109.2cm (43in).*

been doing business in industrial markets since the 1920s, providing machines for road maintenance, light earthmoving and forestry work. In the same year the John Deere Credit Company was established and currently John Deere Credit is one of the 25 largest finance companies in the United States of America.

■ MULTI CYLINDERS

The 30 Series tractors of 1938 were the last two-cylinder machines to be made by John Deere. The company introduced its first four-wheel-drive tractor – the 8010 – in 1959 and then for 1960 it launched a completely new line of multi-cylinder engines capable of meeting the growing demands for more

powerful tractors. The new tractors were unveiled in Dallas, Texas in August 1959. There were four models, 1010, 2010, 3010 and 4010, and they were completely new. The smaller models were powered by in-line four-cylinder engines and the larger ones by an in-line six-cylinder engine. "Johnny Popper" had gone the way of the horse.

■ JOHN DEERE 4010

The six-cylinder 4010 and four-cylinder 3010 were offered as diesels, although both gasoline and LPG versions were available. The tractors were designed to have higher operating speeds and a

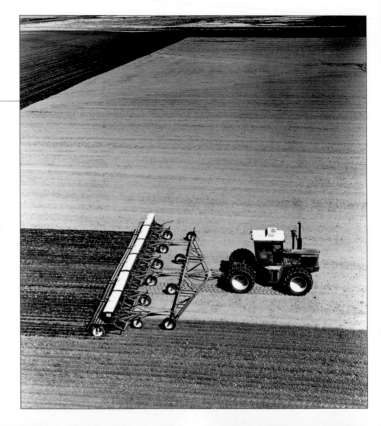

better power-to-weight ratio to increase productivity. The 4010 produced more than 70 drawbar hp while the smaller 3010 achieved more than 50hp. Power steering, power brakes and power implement raising were up-to-the-minute features and an eight-speed transmission enhanced the versatility of the machines. The smaller models in the range, the 1010 and 2010, had features such as adjustable track to make them suitable for row crop work. The tractors were immediately greeted with acclaim and sales were very successful. The new range accounted for a significant increase in John Deere's market share over a five-year period. In 1959 John Deere had 23 per cent of the US tractor market and by 1964 the figure had increased to 34 per cent. This pushed Deere into the position of market leader.

In 1963, in a move to a related, if smaller, type of machinery, Deere

■ TOP *The John Deere 7520 was developed by John Deere during the 1960s and relied on the economies of scale offered in large acreage farming.*

■ ABOVE *A two-wheel-drive John Deere 3040 tractor in an English farmyard. It features a curved windscreen for enhanced visibility for the operator.*

■ LEFT *A 1990s John Deere, equipped with an hydraulic front loader and the standard rear three-point linkage to maximize versatility.*

entered the lawn and grounds care business. During the second half of the 1960s the company's industrial equipment line was expanded to include motor graders, four-wheel-drive loaders, log skidders, backhoe loaders, forklifts and excavators. New models of elevating scrapers, utility crawler dozers and loaders were all introduced. In 1969 John Deere entered the insurance business with the formation of the John Deere Insurance Group, which also offers credit-related insurance products for John Deere dealers.

■ **THE 1970S**
From 1970 onwards there were broad expansions throughout the equipment divisions of John Deere, with major advancements in all product lines, worldwide market development, and a programme of capital investment to enlarge and improve facilities. More than $1.5 billion was invested in this programme between 1975 and 1981.

At this time the 40 Series tractors were becoming more popular as by now they were being assembled with V6

■ LEFT *A four-wheel-drive John Deere 7520 fitted with dual tyres.*

■ LEFT *A hard worked John Deere tractor, fitted with a Farmhand bale and silage grapple.*

■ BELOW *A John Deere 4055 tractor towing a forage harvester, which is blowing hay into the trailer it is also pulling.*

turbocharged diesel engines that produced in excess of 100bhp. This figure was exceeded by the end of the next decade, when John Deere's 4955 Model tractor produced 200bhp. The 7800 has dual rear wheels at each side and a 7636cc/466cu in engine that

produces 170bhp and drives through a 20 speed transmission. In 1978 sales had reached $4 billion, which represented a quadrupling of sales over the previous ten years. Expansion of the credit business continued in 1984 with the acquisition of Farm Plan, that

■ RIGHT *One of the important design considerations with four-wheel-drive tractors is the turning radius. This figure is the official SAE standard for measuring tractor turning and so making comparisons between models.*

offered credit for agricultural purchases, including, for the first time, non-John Deere products.

■ **THE 40 SERIES**

The 1986 John Deere Model 2040 was powered by an engine of 3900cc/238cu in displacement using diesel fuel and producing power in the region of 70hp. It was one of the 40 series of three tractors: the 1640, 2040 and 2140

■ LEFT *In the early 1960s John Deere diversified into the lawn and grounds care business.*

■ BELOW *The 1998 John Deere 7810 model is powered by a turbocharged diesel engine.*

models. Also made in the same year was the John Deere Model 4450 of 7600cc/464cu in displacement that produced 160hp and featured a 15-speed transmission with a part-time 4×4 facility. Diversification continued in 1987 when John Deere entered the golf and turf equipment market and again in 1988 when the company diversified into recreational vehicle and marine markets. In the same year a worldwide Parts Division was established to increase sales of spare parts to owners of both John Deere and other makes of equipment. In 1989, John Deere Maximizer combine harvesters were introduced. In 1991 the worldwide Lawn and Grounds Care Division was established as a separate division within the company, in order to distinguish the specialist products from those of the agricultural equipment business.

■ **THE 8000 SERIES**

The 1990s were auspicious. 1992 saw the introduction of an entirely new line of 66 to 145hp tractors, the 6000 and 7000 Series, designed from the ground up as a complete range of products to meet the varying demands of worldwide markets and to facilitate on-going product updates quickly and at minimum cost. In 1993, the company's 75th year in the tractor business, the tractor line spanned a range from 40 to 400hp. Under a distribution agreement reached in 1993 with Zetor, a tractor manufacturer in the Czech Republic, Deere became the distributor of a lower-priced line of 40 to 85hp tractors in emerging markets, starting with selected areas of Latin America and Asia.

The 8000 Series tractors set new standards for power, performance, manoeuvrability, visibility, control and comfort in 1994. The 8400 was the world's first 225hp row crop tractor. In

■ ABOVE *A Cotton Picker picking the cotton off the plants with the spindle units and transferring the balls into the basket.*

■ BELOW LEFT *John Deere tractors feature a curved tempered glass area.*

■ BELOW *Late 1990s John Deere tractors are equipped with what the manufacturers describe as the ComfortGard cab. It is ergonomically designed so that controls are conveniently positioned.*

■ LEFT *Dual tyres as fitted on this 8850 model have to be weighted, balanced and correctly inflated to increase productivity, reduce soil compaction and optimize minmum fuel consumption.*

by John Deere" for distribution through John Deere dealers and national retailers. In that year it also announced the "GreenStar Combine Yield-Mapping System" as the first in a series of precision-farming systems that was designed to help measure crop yield in different parts of a field.

■ **STOCKS AND SHARES**
The company made significant financial moves in 1995 when stock was split three-for-one from 17 November, 1995. The previous stock split had been a two-for-one split in 1976. In this year the company's consolidated net sales and revenues exceeded $10 billion. Financial moves continued in 1996 when the Board authorized a $500 million share repurchase. For the year

■ BELOW *A two-wheel-drive 65hp (49.2kW) John Deere 6110 model, fitted with the ComfortGard cab. Also available with an open operator station and ROPS bar.*

the same year Deere acquired Homelite, a manufacturer of hand-held and walk-behind power products for both the home-owner and commercial markets. Then in 1995 the company introduced a new line of mid-priced lawn tractors and walk-behind mowers branded as "Sabre

■ ABOVE *The 8400 tractor is the largest model in the John Deere 8000 Series.*

■ RIGHT *The John Deere Advantage Series of tractors. From left they are the 7405, 6605 and 6405 models producing 105, 95 and 85hp respectively.*

■ BELOW *The John Deere 1860 No-Till Air Drill's no-till opener features no-tool adjustments and minimum maintenance.*

■ LEFT *The John Deere 9610 row crop combine harvester is one of the company's Ten Series of combines and is powered by a six-cylinder, turbocharged diesel engine of 496cu in (8.1 litres) displacement.*

■ BELOW LEFT *Combine harvesters such as this make harvesting a one-person operation.*

Deere's consolidated net sales and revenues were a record $11.2 billion. In the same year the Lawn and Grounds Care Division name was changed to Commercial and Consumer Equipment Division. 1995 was successful for tractor and harvester manufacture too with both

the largest introduction of new agricultural products in the company's history and the largest single John Deere agricultural sale ever. This was an order worth $187 million for combine harvesters to be supplied to the Ukraine. Although John Deere is an American

tractor manufacturer, the company has production plants in other countries including Argentina, Australia, Germany, Mexico, South Africa and Spain.

■ **DEERE'S LEGACY**

The importance of John Deere's contribution to agriculture (and America's development) is indicated by the degree of veneration attached to the site of his original smithy in Grand Detour, Illinois. In 1962, an archaeological team from the University of Illinois unearthed the exact location of the blacksmith's shop where John Deere developed his first successful steel plough in 1837. The location has been preserved in an exhibit hall which shows how the dig was performed and contains artefacts found on the site. The centre contains numerous exhibits, including a reconstruction of John Deere's blacksmith shop enhanced with the sounds of horses' hooves on the treadmill, hammers on the anvil and

JOHN DEERE 9400 TRACTOR	
Year	1997
Engine	In-line six-cylinder turbo diesel
Power	425hp (316kW)
Transmission	12 speed (24 speed optional)
Weight	33,770lbs (13,295kg)

■ TOP *The John Deere 9300 is a 360hp tractor with four-whee- drive capability and a range of three optional transmissions.*

■ ABOVE *The 9300 is one model in John Deere's 9000 Series that offers power outputs that range from 260- to 425hp. They are designed to maximize visibility.*

■ RIGHT *The 9400 can be fitted with dual (seen here) or triple tyre combinations that offer optimum traction and minimum soil compaction.*

conversations between workers. It was in a place such as this that John Deere developed the self-polishing steel plough that opened the prairie to agriculture. His home has been preserved to provide a glimpse of pioneer life. Deere built it when he arrived in Grand Detour in 1836 and later added extensions to accommodate his growing family. The rooms are furnished as they would have been then, and show how pioneers cooked, cleaned, bathed and spent their leisure hours. The home of Deere's neighbour, furnished with many period items, has also been preserved and provides a different perspective of early prairie life, as well as serving as a visitor centre.

LANDINI

The eponymous Landini company – the oldest established tractor manufacturer in Italy – was founded by Giovanni Landini, a blacksmith who set up his own business in Fabbrico in Italy's Po Valley. As early as 1884, Giovanni Landini began a mechanical engineering concern in that small Emilian town. His business was successful and gradually he progressed from simple blacksmithing to fabricating machinery for local farms. He produced winemaking machinery, then steam engines, internal combustion engines and crushing equipment. In 1911 Landini built a portable steam engine and from here he progressed to semi-diesel-engined machines. The way forward to a modern and mechanized agricultural industry in Italy was clear and Landini started work on his own design of tractor. His death in 1925 prevented his completion of the first prototype Landini tractor.

■ LEFT *The Velite of the 1930s was one of the Landini company's first successful tractors. It was powered by a 7222cc single-cylinder semi-diesel engine.*

Giovanni Landini's sons took over the business and saw the completion of the tractor project. In 1925 the three sons built the first authentic Italian tractor, a 30hp machine. It was a success and was the forerunner of the viable range of Landini 40 and 50hp models which appeared in the mid-1930s and were to become renowned under the names of Velite, Buffalo and Super. The first production tractors were powered by a

■ ABOVE LEFT *In the post war years Landini manufactured the L25 tractor. It was powered by a 4300cc semi-diesel engine and produced 25hp.*

■ LEFT *This is a 1954 model Landini L25. The semi-diesel engine was capable of running on remarkably poor grade fuels including vegetable oil, creosote and used engine oil.*

■ RIGHT *The 130 Legend incorporates state-of-the-art engine and transmission management techniques.*

■ BELOW *A 1996 Landini 9880 model with a 3870cc displacement engine which produces 88hp.*

40hp semi-diesel engine which was a two-stroke single-cylinder unit. The company continued to produce semi-diesel-engined tractors until 1957, since this type of engine was popular in many European countries, including Germany. For a period Landini and other Italian makers, such as Deganello and Orsi, produced Lanz machines under licence.

In the early 1930s the Landini brothers designed a more powerful tractor which they named the Super Landini: in 1934 it was the most powerful tractor on the Italian market. It produced 50hp at 650 rpm through an engine displacement of 1220cc/74.4cu in. The tractor was driven through a three-speed transmission with a single reverse gear and it stayed in production until the outbreak of World War II.

Following the war the Fabbrico factory both redesigned its range of tractors and expanded the company's output. In the

post-war years the L25 was announced, a 4300cc/262.3cu in displacement semi-diesel engined tractor that produced 25hp. It was made in a new Landini factory in Como, Italy. Production of the 55L model, the most powerful tractor to be equipped with the single -cylinder "Testa Calda" (hot-bulb) engine, started in 1955.

Another key aspect of this redesign was the replacement of the "Testa

Calda" engine used until then, with English manufactured multi-cylinder Perkins diesel power units. It marked Landini's first step towards becoming an international concern. This was later consolidated further through the agreement signed with Massey-Ferguson in 1960, by which Landini became part of the Massey-Ferguson company. As the trend towards full diesel engines continued, Landini entered an agreement with the British company Perkins in 1957 to produce its diesels in Italy under licence. This agreement between Landini and Perkins Engines of Peterborough has endured, as they are still used and are now fitted across the entire Landini range.

In 1959 the C35 model was the first Landini crawler tractor to be manufactured and the precursor of another tradition – crawler machines – that continues to the present time. The renowned 6500, 7500 and 8500 Series models were introduced in 1973 with a redesigned transmission. With the launch of the 500 Series of two- and four-wheel-drive machines in the same year, Landini advanced its wheeled tractors by applying engineering that was to remain standard for years to come. Once the four-wheel-drive models were proven, work began on the design

■ LEFT *The current Landini tractor range encompasses fifty different models that range in power from 43 to 123 PTO hp. This is the Advantage 65F model.*

■ BELOW *Landini has constructed a number of compact tractors, and collaborates with Iseki of Japan.*

of high-powered machines, aimed at producing power in excess of 100hp using in-line, six-cylinder Perkins engines. The range was widened to give tractors with power outputs from 45 up to 145hp. In 1977 production of this new series of tractors commenced.

The 1980s saw the company diversifying its products as well as specializing. Having identified the requirements of the growing wine and fruit production sector, Landini started production of the Series Vineyard, Orchard, Standard and Wide models, the V, F and L machines. Landini soon had a 25 per cent share of the worldwide market and was established as a leading manufacturer of these products. In 1986 Landini launched a new Vineyard tractor range which allowed the Fabbrico factory to become the sole supplier of orchard and vineyard versions of both crawler and wheeled tractors branded as Massey-Fergusons. In 1988 the company launched a redesigned series of tractors, the 60, 70, 80 Series. It achieved a sales record that year for the Fabbrico factory, retailing more than 13,000 tractors.

In 1989 Massey-Ferguson sold 66 per cent of its Landini shares to the

Eurobelge/ Unione Manifatture holding company. This company later sold the controlling interest in its affairs to the Cameli Gerolimich Group. The move took Landini SpA into Unione Manifatture and into the 1990s at the forefront of the tractor industry, both in Italy and worldwide. Landini redesigned its tractors and offered a new range with the launch of the Trekker, Blizzard and

Advantage Series. The result was that for the first time, sales of Landini tractors exceeded 3000 units in the company's export markets.

In February 1994 Valerio and Pierangelo Morra, as representatives of the Argo SpA family holding company, became president and vice-president of Landini SpA respectively. They and Massey-Ferguson contributed to a substantial recapitalization of Landini and in March 1994 Iseki joined Landini SpA. In December of the same year, Landini SpA announced a net profit of 7 billion Lire and an increase in tractor sales of more than 30 per cent over the previous year. Change continued into the following year when in January 1995 Landini acquired Valpadana SpA, a prestigious trademark in the Italian agricultural machinery sector. During the following month the company made an agreement for the distribution of Landini products in North America through the established AGCO sales network, and renewed the agreement for

SUPER LANDINI	
Year	1934
Engine	74.4cu in
Power	50hp at 650rpm
Transmission	Three speed, one reverse
Weight	n/k

the sole supply of specialized wheeled and crawler tractors to AGCO. Overseas markets were not ignored and in March 1995 Landini Sud America was opened in Valencia, Venezuela. This company was aimed at promoting the Landini brand in Latin America, a market that was considered to have potential for sales of tractors. In 1995 Landini sales, including those of imported Massey-Ferguson tractors and the Valpadana tractors manufactured in the San Martino plant, reached a total of 14,057 units, of which 9415 machines were sold under the Landini name.

In 1996, in order to meet the growing demand for the Legend Series of tractors, a significant investment was made when assembly line Number 2 in the Fabbrico factory was dismantled and replaced with a new assembly line, designed to double the factory's production capacity. In San Martino a new factory was opened in 1996, entirely dedicated to machining operations, gear manufacture and prototype component assembly. The presidents of both the Landini and Iseki companies were at the opening of the new plant, signalling agreement between the two companies on long-term technological co-operation between Landini and Iseki.

The current Landini range includes 50 different models, with power outputs ranging from 43–123 PTO hp. Landini tractors are distributed in North

America by AGCO and the current range includes the following models: Advantage, V, F and GT Series, HC Series, Trekker Series, 60 Series, 80 Series, Blizzard, Legend and Globus Series.

■ ABOVE *This compact Landini is working with a round baler on a hill meadow.*

■ LEFT *Traditionally narrow tractors have been used in vineyards, and this Landini Discovery, with a specialist loader, is suitable for between rows.*

■ BELOW *The Landini Discovery 85 compact tractor has many features of larger tractors, including a ROPS roll-over protection cab, and a suspension operator seat.*

OTHER MAKES

(Lamborghini, Land Rover, Lanz, Laverda)

■ LAMBORGHINI

This company is perhaps better known for the production of sports cars than of tractors. Ferruccio Lamborghini was born in Renazzo di Cento, near Ferrara, on 28 April, 1916. His enthusiasm for machinery led him to study mechanical engineering in Bologna, after which he served during World War II as a mechanic in the Italian army's Central Vehicle Division in Rhodes. On his return to Italy at the end of the war, Lamborghini began to purchase surplus military vehicles which he then converted into agricultural machines. Three years after the end of the war, the Lamborghini tractor factory was designing and building its own tractors.

It is hard to say what made Lamborghini turn his attention from agricultural machinery to luxury sports cars. He may have been motivated by the success of his neighbour, Enzo Ferrari. However, folklore, possibly apocryphal, suggests that the idea came to him after a discussion with Enzo Ferrari, when Lamborghini complained about the noisy gearbox in his Ferrari. Ferrari's reply was allegedly that Lamborghini should stick to tractors and let Ferrari build sports cars.

Ferruccio Lamborghini extended his interests into various fields of engineering, including heating and air conditioning systems and even helicopter design. While the cars, which were added to the

■ LEFT AND BELOW *By the time the Lamborghini 950 Premium tractor was manufactured, the car-and-tractor making portions of Lamborghini's business had been sold to separate companies.*

■ BOTTOM LEFT *This four-wheel-drive 874-90 Lamborghini tractor is powered by a turbocharged diesel engine.*

Lamborghini line in 1963, were extremely successful and are still in production, the attempts to manufacture helicopters were hindered due to complex bureaucratic controls imposed by the government, and as a result, the idea was abandoned.

The Lamborghini 5C was a crawler tractor unveiled at the Paris Agricultural Show in 1962. The tractor was unusual in that, as well as crawler tracks, it had three rubber-tyred wheels that allowed use on the road as the wheels lifted the tracks clear of the road surface. The tracks were driven from the rear sprockets and it was to these sprockets that the wheels were attached for

driving on the road. The small front wheel was effectively an idler and steering was achieved by moving the same levers that slewed the tractor around when using tracks. The 5C was powered by a three-cylinder diesel engine that produced 39hp.

When it became clear to Ferruccio Lamborghini that his son Antonio had little interest in the automobile business, he began to contemplate retirement. In 1973 Lamborghini sold all his companies and retired to his vineyard in Umbria, dedicating the last twenty years of his life to the production of fine wines. It was here, at the age of 77, that Lamborghini died on 20 February 1993.

In 1972 the car and tractor portions of Lamborghini's business had been split. The tractor production operations were taken over by Same which has continued to develop the Lamborghini range and increased the volume of production.

■ LAND ROVER

In the early post-war years Rover, which had a reputation for building quality motor cars, was in a difficult position because of the shortage of steel. Rover engineers Maurice Wilks and his brother Spencer considered building a small utility vehicle with an aluminium body and four-wheel drive. The intention was that the machine, specifically intended for agricultural use, would merely be a stopgap until sufficient steel was available for the company to return to building luxury cars.

The Wilks brothers delegated much of the design work of the utility machine. The first prototype Land Rovers had a tractor-like centre steering wheel to enable them to be sold in either left- or right-hand drive markets. Because a conventional chassis would have required expensive tooling, the engineer Olaf Poppe devised a jig on which four strips of flat steel could be welded together to form a box-section chassis.

The first Land Rover, with a 2m/80in wheelbase, was shown to the public at the 1948 Amsterdam Motor Show. Orders flowed in, especially when early Land Rovers were displayed at agricultural shows around Britain, and the company began to look seriously at export markets. The vehicles were demonstrated ploughing and driving mowers. Power take-offs and winches were optional extras and between 1948 and 1954 numerous details were refined and improved. To make the vehicle

■ ABOVE *The prototype Land Rover with its centre steering position, operating a Massey-Harris elevator during the construction of a haystack, in 1947.*

■ BELOW *A Series II Land Rover, adapted to tow an especially designed swan neck articulated trailer, seen here loaded with a Perkins diesel-powered tractor.*

more capable it was redesigned for 1954: the wheelbase was increased by 15-cm/6-in and the rear overhang increased by 7.5cm/3in. This enabled the rear load area to be increased. A long wheelbase variant, at 2.7m/107in, was also made available as a pick-up and these models had the 1997cc/121.8cu in engine which had been available in the later 2m/80in models. Changes were again made to the Land Rover for 1956 when both models were stretched another 5cm/2in to give wheelbases of 2.24m/88in and 2.77m/109in. The diesel engine was introduced in June 1957 and by 1958 Rover had produced in excess of 200,000 Land Rovers. In April 1958 the company introduced the so-called Series II Land Rover. The Series II featured a redesigned body that was 4cm/1½in wider than its predecessors, together with other minor improvements including more modern door hinges and bonnet latches.

While Land Rover products are still made and widely exported, the emphasis of the range is now on sport utility vehicles, with the exception of the Defender 90 and

■ LEFT *The most modern version of the Land Rover is the Defender 90, still widely used by farmers, although the company's more luxurious models are considered as sport utility vehicles (SUVs).*

OTHER MAKES

110 Models, which are refined versions of
the original Land Rovers and are still
popular for agricultural applications.
Numerous specialized agricultural
conversions have been made to Land Rover
vehicles during the course of their
production to suit them to specific tasks,
such as carrying and operating implements,
in the manner of the Mercedes Unimog.

■ LANZ

In Germany, Lanz produced Bulldog
tractors including the Model T crawler and
the L, N and P wheeled models offering 15,
23 and 45bhp respectively. The machines
were imported into Britain and were
popular because of their ability to run on
low-grade fuel, including used engine and
gearbox oil thinned with paraffin. In 1924
Ford upped the ante when the Fordson F
tractor went on sale in Germany, meaning
that German manufacturers had to compete.
The differing types of fuel employed by
Ford and the German manufacturers
illustrated a divergence of ideas about
tractors. The German companies, such as
Stock and Hanomag, compared the
Fordson's fuel consumption unfavourably
with that of their own machines, which were

moving towards diesel fuel. Lanz
introduced the Feldank tractor, that was
capable of running on poor fuel through
its use of a semi-diesel engine.

The initial Bulldogs were crude. The HL
model, for example, had no reverse gear:
the engine was stalled and run backwards
to enable the machine to be reversed.

■ ABOVE *Lanz built
farm machinery from
1859 and its Bulldog
tractor was regarded as
a simple, reliable
machine. Prior to World
War II Lanz was one of
the two major German
tractor makers.*

■ LEFT *Lanz Bulldog
production was resumed
after World War II,
despite the company's
factory being razed to
the ground by Allied
bombing. The post-war
political situation in
Germany affected
Lanz's sales adversely.*

Power came from a single horizontal-cylinder two-stroke semi-diesel engine that produced 12hp. The HL was gradually improved, becoming the HR2 in 1926. Lanz was later acquired by John Deere.

■ LAVERDA

Laverda was founded in 1873 in Breganze, Italy, and by the beginning of this century had become the leading Italian manufacturer of threshing machines. The company is also noted for its production of motorcycles. In 1975 Fiat Trattori became a shareholder in Laverda, then in 1984 Fiat Trattori became Fiatagri, the Fiat group's holding company for the agricultural machinery sector.

■ LEYLAND

In Great Britain, Morris Motors eventually became part of the British Leyland conglomerate. This company was concerned by poor sales of Nuffield tractors, so renamed the brand as British Leyland. Along with this renaming, a new two-tone blue colour scheme was adopted for the tractors.

British Leyland built tractors such as the 270 and 344 models. However, the tractor maker did not have sufficient funds to develop its products and it was gradually overtaken in sales by other tractor makers. Leyland tractors was sold in 1981 and joined with Marshall as a part of the Nickerson organization.

■ ABOVE *A late-1970s British Leyland 344 tractor, in the two-tone blue colour scheme favoured by BL after it had acquired Nuffield as part of the merger with Morris Motors.*

■ RIGHT *The British Leyland badge on the front of this 344 tractor could also be seen on a variety of cars during the 1970s.*

■ BELOW LEFT *Lanz Bulldogs were manufactured in Mannheim, Germany, but when John Deere had acquired the company production the long-running model was halted.*

■ BELOW *This decaying British Leyland tractor retains its factory-fitted safety cab.*

MASSEY-FERGUSON

■ LEFT *A 1970s Massey-Ferguson 135 photographed in Cappadocia, Turkey.*

In 1953 Harry Ferguson merged his company with the Massey-Harris company. As the deal was being finalized, there arose the question of which exchange rate was to be used. Harry suggested settling the matter with the toss of a coin. He lost the toss, and about a million dollars, but appeared not to care, no doubt realizing that his patents and equipment were in capable hands.

Once Harry Ferguson had sold his tractor company to Massey-Harris the face of tractor manufacturing was profoundly altered. Before the merger the Massey-Harris company had been competing with both Ford and Ferguson. For a while the newly formed Massey-Harris-Ferguson company produced two

MASSEY FERGUSON MF 362 4WD	
Year	1998
Engine	Perkins four cylinder diesel
Power	60 PTO hp, 62bhp
Transmission	Eight forward, two reverse
Weight	5877lbs (2666kg)

■ ABOVE LEFT *Massey-Harris was noted for the manufacture of self-propelled combine harvesters, and neglected tractor development to a degree. To catch up they merged with Ferguson in 1953.*

■ LEFT *The 1970s styling of the Massey-Ferguson range was much more angular than that which went before, as evidenced by the line of hood and grille on this MF135 model.*

■ RIGHT *A little
modified, probably
repainted more
than once, but still
working more than
thirty years after it
was made.*

■ LEFT *The two-wheel-drive MF 399 has
16 inch diameter front wheels, and 38 inch
diameter rear ones. It is powered by a six-
cylinder Perkins diesel, and has a 12
speed transmission.*

■ BELOW LEFT TOP *The four-wheel-
drive version of the Massey-Ferguson
MF 362. This tractor is powered by a
naturally aspirated, four-cylinder Perkins
A4.236 engine.*

■ BELOW LEFT BOTTOM *A dilapidated MF
20 during a break from haymaking.*

■ BELOW RIGHT *A four-cylinder, Perkins
diesel-engined Massey-Ferguson 375,
donated by the World Business Council to
farmers in Tanzania, East Africa.*

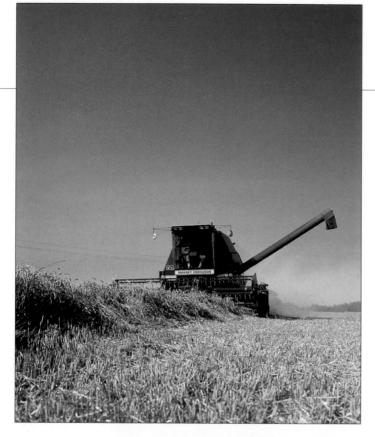

separate lines of tractors, continuing with both the Massey-Harris and the Ferguson makes, as both tractors had loyal followers amongst dealers and customers. The MH50 and Ferguson 40 had different bodywork but were mechanically identical as both models were based on the Ferguson 35. In November 1957 the now Massey-Ferguson Company produced its first "Red and Grey" tractor, the Model MF35 powered by Perkins engines.

The company was Canadian-based and produced tractors all around the

MASSEY FERGUSON MF 32 CONVENTIONAL COMBINE	
Year	1998
Engine	Valmet 620DSL
Power	129kW (175 DIN hp)
Transmission	Hydrostatic
Weight	22,706lbs (8939kg)

■ ABOVE *Combine harvesters are required to cut the standing crop, then lift it on to the conveyor which takes it to the rasps, which then remove the grain from the straw.*

■ RIGHT *This Massey-Ferguson combine from the 1960s carried out the same task, but the styling of combines and provision of operator comfort were still ahead in the future.*

■ LEFT *This Massey-Ferguson 530 S combine harvester features an open operator station, something that is becoming rarer as cab technology continually progresses.*

■ BELOW *This MF 31 combine was the largest one in the Massey-Ferguson range in 1986 and was powered by a 153hp, turbocharged Perkins engine.*

■ ABOVE
Combines, like tractors, need to maintain traction in fields, but rely on hydrostatic transmissions connected to their large capacity diesel engines.

■ RIGHT *For harvesting on fields with slopes of up to 11 degrees, Massey-Ferguson has devised the Auto Level system, designed to keep an even spread across the machine's grain-separating components.*

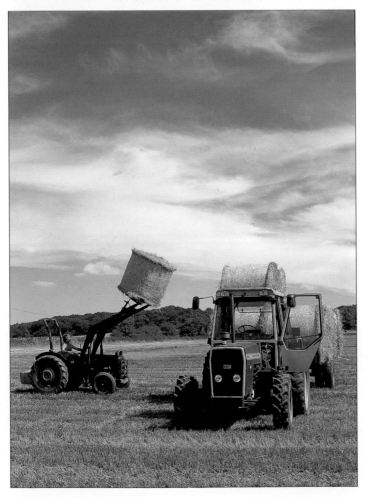

■ ABOVE LEFT *A Massey-Ferguson 3070 tractor, with a Cambridge roller, preparing the land for the next year's crop.*

■ ABOVE RIGHT *A four-wheel-drive Massey-Ferguson tractor, equipped with a hydraulic front loader. This is a versatile and perennially popular farmyard tool.*

■ LEFT *Two generations of Massey-Ferguson tractors at work. The older model is being used to load round hay bales on to the trailer, pulled behind the newer four-wheel-drive model.*

■ BELOW *The Massey-Ferguson 2775 tractor of the 1980s features a V8 Perkins engine of 640cu in displacement.*

■ RIGHT *The four-wheel-drive MF 6180, of 1998, is powered by a Perkins 1006-6T engine, a six-cylinder turbo diesel unit that drives through a gearbox offering 16 forward and reverse gears.*

world. The all-new MF35 was followed by a range of tractors including the MF50, MF65 and MF85. In 1976 Massey-Ferguson introduced new tractors, the 1505 and 1805 Models, both powered by the 174hp Caterpillar V8 diesel engine.

In the mid-1980s the 3000 Series of Massey-Ferguson machines was made available with a turbo-diesel, 190hp, six-cylinder engine. A smaller Massey-Ferguson tractor was the MF 398, powered by a 3867cc/236cu in diesel engine and featuring a 4x4 transmission. Two Massey-Ferguson tractors from 1986 were the Models 2685 and MF699. The former had a 5800cc/353.8cu in Perkins turbo-diesel engine that produced 142 hp and was one of the 2005 Series of three tractors: 2645, 2685 and 2725. Each had a four-wheel-drive trans-mission that incorporated 16 forward and 12 reverse gears. The MF699 was the most powerful in the MF600 Series of four tractors, MF675, 690, 698T and 699. It was powered by a 100hp engine.

Massey-Ferguson itself became part of AGCO in 1994. According to the manu-facturer, "For 33 straight years more people have purchased MF tractors than

■ LEFT *A 1993 MF 3095 Autotronic. This is one of the 3000 series of tractors that was among the first Massey-Ferguson tractors to make extensive use of electronics.*

■ BELOW *The Massey-Ferguson MF 3690 Autotronic was another of the 3000 series of tractors of 1993.*

■ ABOVE *The MF 185 is an American-made rectangular baler, designed to be towed behind a tractor. It is capable of producing bales of up to 320kg (700lbs). It rides on wide flotation tyres.*

■ LEFT *The MF 844 loader is one of the 800 series loaders, designed to be used in conjunction with 60 – 90hp tractors. It can lift 1700kg (4318lbs) to a maximum height of 3.75 metres (12.3ft).*

MASSEY-FERGUSON MF 4245 4WD TRACTOR

Year	1998
Engine	Perkins 1004-4T
Power	75.8 PTO hp, 88bhp
Transmission	Eight forward, eight reverse
Weight	3759kg/9548lbs

■ LEFT *A four-wheel-drive Massey Harris 4245 tractor, haymaking with an MF 146 variable chamber round baler.*

■ OPPOSITE *A 1998 six-cylinder 114hp MF 4270 tractor working in conjunction with a Massey-Ferguson Forage Harvester during haymaking.*

■ RIGHT *The MF 40 conventional combine has a section where grain is stored after the threshing and separating processes. A Valmet 612DSJL engine supplies the power.*

■ BELOW *The MF 8120, seen here in four-wheel-drive form, has a six cylinder turbo diesel engine driving it through a 32 speed transmission.*

any other brand." Massey-Ferguson's current range is comprehensive and includes tractors offering 130–180 PTO hp, 86–110 PTO hp, 55–95 PTO hp, 34–67 PTO hp, 37–53 PTO hp and 16–40 engine hp, as well as conventional combine harvesters, rotary combine harvesters and loaders.

The 130–180 PTO hp tractors in the 8100 Series are designed as high-performance tractors, while the 4200 Series 55–95 PTO hp tractors are available as a selection of models of varying configurations with different

options and attachments. The 200 Series of 34–67 PTO hp tractors features Perkins diesel engines. Another small range of tractors from Massey-Ferguson is the 1200 16–40 PTO hp Series. Massey-Ferguson manufactures Class 5 and 6 combine harvesters, including the 8680 conventional and 8780 rotary combines.

■ BELOW *The MF 6130 is a 1998 model tractor with a 16 forward and reverse speed transmission. Power comes from a four-cylinder turbo diesel engine.*

MASSEY- HARRIS

■ BELOW *One of the earliest four-wheel-drive tractors was the Massey-Harris General Purpose of 1930. A 226cu in displacement engine powered it.*

■ BOTTOM *The Massey-Harris 101 was introduced in 1938 as a streamlined row crop tractor. It is powered by a high compression, gasoline-fuelled Chrysler six-cylinder engine.*

Massey-Harris was formed in 1891 in Toronto, Canada from the merger of two companies who manufactured farm implements. Daniel Massey had been making implements since 1847 while A. Harris, Son & Company were competitors for the same market. The Model 25 was a popular tractor through the 1930s and 40s. Another Massey-Harris tractor of this era was the 101 of 1935. This machine was driven by a 24hp Chrysler in-line six-cylinder engine. A third was the Twin Power Challenger powered by an I-head four-cylinder engine that produced approximately 36hp. The company chose a red and straw-yellow colour scheme for its tractors in the mid-1930s.

After World War II, Massey-Harris introduced the Model 44 based around the same engine as the pre-war

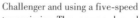

■ BOTTOM *The Massey-Harris Challenger of 1936 was the last from the company to have the Wallis tractor-style boiler plate unit frame. The rear wheels were adjustable to cater for different row widths.*

■ RIGHT *A Massey-Harris combine in Britain during the 1950s.*

■ BELOW RIGHT *The Challenger was rated as a 26-36hp tractor, power came from an in-line, four-cylinder, gasoline engine.*

MASSEY-HARRIS MODEL 101	
Year	1939
Engine	Chrysler L-head T57-503 gasoline
Power	23.94 drawbar hp
Transmission	Three speed
Weight	2597kg/5725lbs

Challenger and using a five-speed transmission. The company brought out a new range in 1947 which still included the Model 44, to which were added the Models 11, 20, 30 and 55. The Model 30 featured a five-speed transmission and more than 32,000 were made before 1953 when the company merged with Ferguson.

The tractor built in the largest numbers by Massey-Harris prior to the merger was the Massey-Harris Pony. This was a small tractor and proved more popular in overseas markets than in the United States and Canada, where it was considered too small for many farming applications. It was produced in the Canadian Woodstock plant from 1947 and at the Marquette factory in France from 1951. A decade later the production total exceeded 121,000. The

■ LEFT *The
Massey-Harris
Pony was produced
in Massey-Harris's
French and
Canadian plants
and production
eventually totalled
in excess of
121,000.*

first version of the Pony was powered by
a four-cylinder Continental engine
driving a three-speed transmission with
one reverse gear. Its top speed was
11kph/7mph and it produced 11hp. The
Pony was basic in its initial form, but
was refined over its production run.
Canadian production was halted in
1954, but in 1957 the 820 Pony was
offered from the French factory with a
five-speed gearbox and a German
Hanomag diesel engine. It was further
refined for 1959, when it was
redesignated the 821 Pony. Around
90,000 of the Pony tractors
manufactured were built in the French
factory and this was Massey-Harris's
first real European success. The post-
war Model 44 had been a success for the
Massey-Harris company in the United
States, where 90,000 were made in

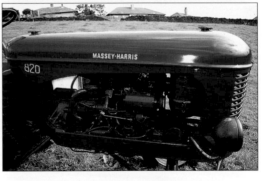

■ LEFT *Many
European manu-
factured Massey-
Harris 820 Ponys
were fitted with
diesel engines
made by Hanomag.*

■ BELOW LEFT *A
distinctive feature
of the 820 Pony
was its rounded
radiator grille.*

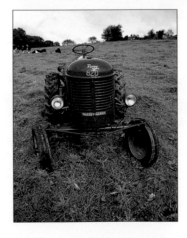

MASSEY-HARRIS MODEL 44	
Year	1949
Engine	Four cylinder I-head
Power	27.75 drawbar hp
Transmission	Three speed
Weight	2307kg/5085lbs

Racine, Wisconsin. It featured the
rounded pre-war styling but was
mechanically new. The customer had a
choice of four-cylinder engines that
used either petrol, paraffin or diesel
fuel. A hydraulic lift system for
implements was introduced in 1950.
The company chose the Model 44 as its
tractor to enter the British market and
started by manufacturing them in
Manchester in 1948, although
operations were later moved north to
Kilmarnock, Scotland. This was largely
an assembly process because the
components were imported from Racine.
The models offered included row crop,
high clearance and Roadless-converted

■ ABOVE *Massey-Harris started production of the 744 PD tractor in Manchester in 1948. Production was later moved to Scotland and the tractor redesignated as the 744D.*

■ BELOW *The Massey-Harris 33 was made between 1952 and 1955. It was an upgraded version of the two plough 30 that had been introduced in 1947.*

half-track versions. Around 17,000 were made in total and in later years approximately 11,000 of a Perkins-engined variant – the 745 – were made before production was halted in 1957. In that year, after the merger with Ferguson, the company was renamed Massey-Ferguson and another new line of tractors was introduced.

The following three examples of results from Nebraska Tractor Tests give an illustration of how the Massey-Harris tractor range progressed in the post-war decades. Nebraska Test Number 306 was on the Massey-Harris Model 101 S made by the Massey-Harris Co, Racine, Wisconsin, and tested between 22 and 26 May 1939. The tractor's equipment consisted of 10–36 rear tyres, 5.00–15 front tyres, a six-cylinder L-head Chrysler T57–503 engine, run at 1500 and 1800rpm, 3.125in bore × 4.375in stroke, and an Auto-Lite electrical system. The tractor's weight was 1726kg/3805lb on steel wheels and 2597kg/5725lb on rubber tyres.

The Test H Data obtained with rubber tyres was as follows: gear: 3, speed: 7.27kph/4.52mph, load: 901.3kg/1987lb, rated load: 23.94 drawbar hp, fuel economy: 9.85hp hours per gallon. The Test H Data on steel wheels was as follows: gear: 2, speed: 5.92kph/3.68mph, load: 844kg/1862lb, rated load: 18.29 drawbar hp, fuel economy: 7.46hp hours per gallon. The fuel economy at 1800rpm maximum with a load of 36.15 belt hp was 10.89 hp

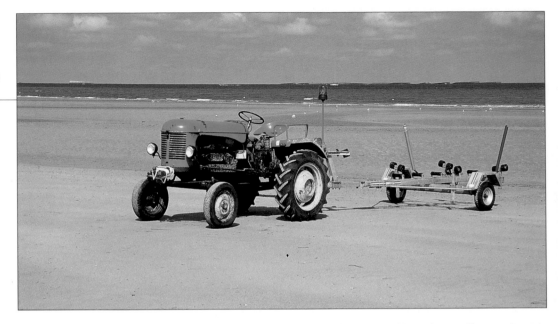

hours per gallon. Fuel economy at 1500rpm with a rated load of 31.5 belt hp yielded 11.86hp hours per gallon.

Nebraska Test Number 427 was carried out on the Massey-Harris 44K Standard made by the Massey-Harris Co, Racine, Wisconsin, and tested between 29 September and 14 October 1949. The tractor's equipment included a four-cylinder I-head engine, 1350rpm, 3.875in bore × 5.5 in stroke, a 6 volt Auto-Lite electrical system, a Zenith 62AJ10 carburettor. The tractor's weight was 2306kg/5085lb and the Test H Data obtained was as follows: gear: 3, speed: 4.29mph, load: 1182kg/2608lb, slippage: 4.4 per cent, rated load: 27.7 drawbar hp, fuel economy: 10.42hp

■ ABOVE *Despite the familiar colours of this tractor on a French beach it is not a John Deere, but a repainted Massey-Harris Pony from the French Marquette factory.*

■ LEFT *The Massey-Harris 745 was a Perkins diesel-powered tractor intended as an improved version of the 744. Approximately 11,000 were made between 1954 and 1958 in the Kilmarnock, Scotland plant.*

■ BELOW *A gasoline-engined version of the European-manufactured Massey-Harris Pony. The engine is an in-line four-cylinder unit.*

hours per gallon. 506kg/1116lb of ballast was added to each rear wheel for tests F, G, and H. Test G resulted in a low-gear maximum pull of 2128kg/ 4692lb. Fuel economy at Test C maximum load of 35.66 belt hp was 11.3hp hours per gallon. Test D rated load of 33.64 belt hp yielded 11.19hp hours per gallon. Tractor fuel was used for the 45.5 hours of engine running time.

Nebraska Test Number 603 was carried out seven years later on a Massey-Harris 333 made by Massey-Harris-Ferguson Inc, Racine, Wisconsin, and was tested between 25 October and 3 November 1956. The tractor's equipment included a four-cylinder I-head engine, 1500rpm, 3.688in bore × 4.875in stroke, 12–38 rear tyres, 6.50–16 front tyres with a tractor weight of 2685kg/5920lb. The Test H Data recorded was: gear: 3, high range, speed: 7.94kph/4.93mph, load: 1026kg/ 2262lb, slippage: 3.76 per cent, rated load: 29.71 drawbar hp, fuel economy: 10.69hp hours per gallon. 466kg/1028lb

of ballast was added to each rear wheel for tests F, G and H. Test G resulted in a low-gear maximum pull of 2452kg/ 5407lb at 2.1kph/1.31mph with a slippage of 12.08 per cent. Fuel economy at Test C maximum load of 39.84 belt hp was 12.37hp hours per gallon.

■ BELOW *One reason that production of the Massey-Harris Pony was continued in Europe, after being halted in Canada, was that the size of the tractor proved more suitable to the smaller scale farms of Europe than those of North America.*

MERCEDES-BENZ

Benz started building tractors in 1919 when it offered the 40 and 80hp gasoline-engined "Land Traktors", but the Benz-Sendling S7 of 1923 was the first diesel-engined tractor manufactured by Benz. It featured power from a 30hp two-cylinder, vertical engine. The machine itself was a three-wheeled tractor with a single driven rear wheel, although outriggers were supplied to ensure stability during use. A four-wheeled machine, the BK, quickly superseded the S7.

■ BENZ AND DAIMLER

In 1926 Benz and Daimler merged, adopting the name Mercedes-Benz. During the 1930s the company

■ ABOVE *The MB-trac 1500 Mercedes Benz tractor is fully reversible which means it can be used as a dual directional tractor by rotating the controls, instruments and seat through 180 degrees in the cab.*

MERCEDES-BENZ U1200 UNIMOG	
Year	1998
Engine	OM 366 A in-line six cylinder 5958cc/ 363cu in
Power	125hp
Transmission	Eight forward, eight reverse
Weight	8500kg/18,739lbs

■ LEFT *The dual directional nature of the MB-trac 1500 means it can be used to push or pull implements where appropriate. A 150hp turbo diesel engine of 5675cc/346cu in displacement provides ample power.*

■ RIGHT *Mercedes-Benz Unimogs are supplied in numerous configurations, and have been manufactured for several decades, offering four-wheel drive.*

produced the OE model that was powered by a horizontally arranged single-cylinder, four-stroke diesel engine that produced 20hp. One of these machines competed in the 1930 World Tractor Trials held in England. Prior to World War II tractor production in Germany was relatively small in scale and even in the coming conflict the German army was to rely heavily on horse-drawn vehicles, in stark contrast to the mechanized armies of the Allies.

In the post-war years two of the first popular and successful tractors were of a four-wheel-drive configuration. One was

■ ABOVE *A short wheel base platform variant U900 Unimog from the mid-1980s. The Unimog is designed to accept a variety of specialist implements.*

■ RIGHT *To enhance ground clearance, the Unimog, such as this 1990s U1200 model, are based on portal axles.*

the MAN 325, that remained in production for two decades until the company shelved tractor production in favour of trucks. The second was the Boehringer Unimog which was later sold to Mercedes-Benz. Mercedes-Benz has continued to produce this machine, still known as the Unimog, for several decades in a variety of configurations including models designed for agricultural use as implement carriers.

■ **MERCEDES UNIMOG**
The Unimog has evolved into the Unimog System of vehicle and implements, based on a wide range of

vehicles and an almost unlimited number of implement attachment options. Several ranges are offered, from compact to heavy-duty models and each has at least three standard implement attachment points and a hydraulic system that ensures implement operation. The Unimog has been designed so that its wheels distribute pressure evenly on the ground in order to minimize soil compaction. It is of all-wheel-drive configuration to ensure optimum traction.

Another advanced Mercedes-Benz tractor was the MB-trac 1500, introduced in 1986. This tractor featured a turbo-diesel engine of 5675cc/346cu in displacement that produced power in the region of 150hp. The MB-trac was designed as a dual-direction tractor.

OTHER MAKES

■ **MINSK**
The Minsk Tractor Works sells its tractors through agricultural machine distributors in 35 countries around the world. Current production includes models such as the MTZ-320, MTZ-682, MTZ-1221 and MTZ-920.

MINNEAPOLIS - MOLINE

■ BELOW *The Minneapolis-Moline Universal Model J was a row crop tractor with infinite rear wheel adjustment, capable on rubber tyres of 12.2mph (19.5kph).*

In the hectic 1920s, many new tractor-making companies were formed while others merged to form new corporations. In 1929 three extant companies, Minneapolis Steel and Machinery, the Minneapolis Threshing Machine Company and the Moline Implement Company, all merged and Minneapolis-Moline Power Implement Company was the result. Amongst these companies' assets were Twin City Tractors and Minneapolis Tractors, and in the wake of the merger came the rationalization of their products and factories. The Twin City tractor range was chosen as the one to spearhead the Minneapolis-Moline push into the market, with production continuing in the Minneapolis factory. Initially the machines were marketed as Twin City tractors with the Minneapolis-Moline name added, but as the range evolved, the Twin City brand name was reduced in prominence and Minneapolis-Moline became the brand name. The constituent companies are detailed here.

■ BELOW *The Minneapolis-Moline Model R was a two-plough tricycle, row crop tractor, manufactured between 1939 and 1941.*

■ MOLINE UNIVERSAL

In 1915 the Moline Plow Company had purchased the Universal Tractor Company of Columbus, Ohio. The product line was moved to Moline, Illinois and a new building was constructed for the production of the Moline Universal Tractor. This was a two-wheel unit designed for use with the farmer's horse-drawn implements as well as with newly developed Moline tractor-drawn implements. The Universal was commonly referred to as the first row crop tractor. It was equipped with electric lights and a starter, components that were considered advanced for the time.

After World War I, a number of automobile manufacturers wanted to produce tractors and the Moline Plow Company was courted by manufacturer John N. Willys. Willys purchased Moline from the owners, the Stephens

MINNEAPOLIS-MOLINE UNIVERSAL MODEL J	
Year	1935
Engine	F-head four cylinder
Power	16hp
Transmission	Five speed
Weight	2222kg/4900lbs

■ BELOW *The Model U was tested in the Nebraska tractor tests in 1938 and produced 30.86 drawbar and 38.12 belt horsepower at 1275rpm.*

family, and subsequently his automobile company began producing the Universal tractor. Willys had as his partners in the tractor trade George N. Peek, a well-known farm equipment executive, and General Hugh Johnson. Willys continued to produce the Moline Universal tractor into the 1920s. In this decade the tractor boom subsided; Willys withdrew from the Moline Plow Company and sold out to his partners. General Johnson became president and R. W. Lea

■ LEFT *The Minneapolis-Moline Model V was a compact tractor. This example was produced in 1944.*

■ BELOW *The Minneapolis-Moline Model Z was introduced in 1937 as a row crop tractor, painted in the new Prairie Gold colour.*

became vice-president of the Moline Plow Company. When they retired their associates took over and operated the business as the Moline Implement Company, which it remained until joining the Minneapolis-Moline organization in 1929.

■ TYPES A AND B

The Minneapolis Threshing Machine Company began producing steam traction engines in 1889 just west of Minneapolis, where the town of Hopkins was founded, and flourished solely because of the company. In 1893, a Victory threshing machine and steam engine built by the company won several medals at the World Exposition in Chicago. By 1911 the Minneapolis Threshing Machine Company was building tractors under the Minneapolis name and went on to build many large tractors before the Minneapolis-Moline merger, but these tractors were better suited to sod-breaking than for row crop applications. After building a couple of row-type tractors the company marketed its Minneapolis 17-30 Type A and Type B. These were cross-motor row crop tractors and remained in production even after the merger. During the 1920s,

even before the Minneapolis-Moline organization, the company's products were advertised as being part of "The Great Minneapolis Line".

In the late 1800s and early 1900s the Minneapolis Steel and Machinery Company was primarily a structural steel producer, turning out thousands of tons per year. The company also produced the Corliss steam engine, that served as a power unit for many flour mills in the Dakotas. In 1910

Minneapolis Steel and Machinery produced a tractor under the Twin City name, the Twin City 40. At the outbreak of World War I, the company was one of the larger tractor producers. It also manufactured a number of tractors under contract, such as the Bull tractor for the Bull Tractor Co. Through the 1920s, Twin City tractors were promoted with slogans such as "Team Of Steel" and "Built To Do The Work". After 1929, this line was still produced in the

■ LEFT
*Minneapolis-Moline
came about from
the merger in 1929
of three companies
involved in the
production of farm
machinery.*

■ RIGHT *The UTS,
like others in the
Minneapolis-Moline
range, was
equipped with red-
painted wheels.*

**MINNEAPOLIS-MOLINE
MODEL U**

Year	1938
Engine	In-line four cylinder
Power	30.86 drawbar and 38.12 belt hp
Transmission	Five speed
Weight	n/k

■ RIGHT *Although the M-M logo stands for
Minneapolis-Moline, the tractor
manufacturers lost no time in using it to
suggest that M-M made Modern Machinery.*

■ BELOW *The Minneapolis-Moline UTS
was a wartime model in the U-series of
tractors. The similar UTU was a tricycle
row crop tractor.*

old Minneapolis Steel and Machinery Lake Street Plant under the Minneapolis-Moline Twin City tractor banner.

In the new Minneapolis-Moline Power Implement Company, two of the major historic agricultural machine-producing cities were represented. After the merger, the Minneapolis-Moline Power Implement Company Officers for 1929 were as follows: J. L. Record (MSM) Chairman of the Board; W. C. Macfarlane (MSM) President and Administrative Officer; George L. Gillette (MSM) Vice-President of Sales; Harold B. Dineen (Moline) Vice-President of Production and Design; N. A. Wiff (MSM) Vice-President; W. C. Rich (MSM) Secretary; W. S. Peddle (MSM) Treasurer. In reality most of the top officers of the three companies were content to retire instead of becoming involved in Minneapolis-Moline Power Implement, preferring that the younger generation take over.

After experiments with the luxury UDLX tractor with an enclosed cab,

■ ABOVE *This 1947 Minneapolis-Moline GTA tractor of 1947 was designed to run on liquid petroleum gas (LPG).*

■ LEFT *Minneapolis-Moline tractors were restyled in the immediate post-war years. This is a restyled, row crop tricycle Model Z from 1949.*

■ LEFT *One of the last new tractors to be added to the M-M range before the outbreak of World War II was the GT, a standard tread tractor that was tested at Nebraska in 1939.*

MINNEAPOLIS-MOLINE M-5	
Year	1960
Engine	5506cc/336cu in Diesel
Power	58.15hp at 1500rpm
Transmission	Six speed
Weight	n/k

Minneapolis-Moline launched the GT as a five-plough tractor in 1939. In the Nebraska Tractor Tests its measured power output was 55hp at the belt, despite being rated at only 49hp by its manufacturer. Powered by a gasoline-fuelled in-line four-cylinder engine, it developed its maximum power at 1075rpm. Later, in the aftermath of World War II, increased power versions, the G and GB Models, were offered.

The White Motor Company purchased Minneapolis-Moline in 1963. AGCO purchased White Tractors in 1991, and in doing so acquired the rights to the Minneapolis-Moline name.

■ ABOVE LEFT *By the time this 1969 M670 tractor had been made, Minneapolis-Moline had been owned by White for six years. The company was later acquired by AGCO.*

■ RIGHT *The fact that this 1970 Minneapolis-Moline G1050 tractor, of 504cu in displacement, is designed to run on LPG gas, is made clear by the provision of a tank in front of the radiator.*

NEW HOLLAND

The New Holland Machine Company was founded in 1895 in Pennsylvania and specialized in the manufacture of agricultural equipment. It endured until 1940 when New Holland changed owners and, following a company reorganization, began production of one of the first successful automatic pick-up hay balers. In 1947 the Sperry Corporation acquired the New Holland Machine Company and formed Sperry New Holland. In 1964 Sperry New Holland purchased a major interest in Claeys, which was by this time one of the largest combine manufacturers in

FORD NEW HOLLAND 8830	
Year	1998
Engine	6571cc/401cu in, diesel
Power	170hp
Transmission	18 forward, nine reverse
Weight	6804kg/15,000lbs

■ BELOW *New Holland is a noted manufacturer of an automatic pickup hay baler. The company expanded its operations by buying a major interest in Claeys, an established European company.*

Europe. Sperry New Holland launched the haybine mower-conditioner, Model 460. This was capable of accomplishing what had previously required two or three machines to do and was perceived as a significant innovation in hay-harvesting technology.

■ MERGER
In 1986 the Ford Motor Company acquired Sperry New Holland and merged it with Ford Tractor Operations, naming the new company Ford New Holland. In 1991 Fiat acquired Ford

■ RIGHT *During the 1970s companies such as Case, Claas and New Holland began to dominate the increasingly international European market.*

New Holland Inc, merged it with FiatGeotech and named the new company N. H. Geotech. In 1993 this company was renamed New Holland. At its second worldwide convention held in Orlando, Florida, New Holland launched 24 tractor models in three different ranges alongside the Fiat-Hitachi Compact Line.

The articulated tractors in the Versatile 82 Series are high-powered machines designed for the biggest of fields and the heaviest applications. The range includes the Models 9282, 9482, 9682 and 9882, all of which are powered by six-cylinder engines of varying horsepower with twelve-speed transmissions in both two- and four-wheel-drive configurations. The Series 70 tractors have power outputs that range between 170 and 240hp. They incorporate New Holland's own "PowerShift" transmission which offers single lever control of the 18 forward

■ ABOVE *A New Holland 8070 combine harvester loading a trailer with the grain which has been threshed and separated in the combine.*

■ RIGHT *A New Holland combine in Wiltshire, England during the harvest. The few weeks of the harvest are crucial to the economics of the farming year, and the cost effective-ness of combine harvesters.*

and nine reverse gears. They are manufactured in Winnipeg, Canada and marketed worldwide. The tractors are available with or without cab, or with ROPS (Rollover Protection Structure). The third range of New Holland tractors is the 90 Series, whose models have a range of transmissions. The 100–90 and 110–90 Models are manufactured in Jesi, Italy while the 140–90, 160–90 and 180–90 Models are manufactured in Curitiba, Brazil.

In 1997 New Holland completed its purchase of Ford Motor Credit Company's partnership interests in the

NEW HOLLAND NH 6635	
Year	1996
Engine	Turbo diesel
Power	85hp (63 kW)
Transmission	Optional with creeper
Weight	n/k

two joint ventures that provide financing for New Holland's products in the United States. New Holland also signed an agreement with Manitou, for the design and production of a New Holland

range of telescopic handlers. In India in 1998, New Holland completed the construction of a new plant for the manufacture of tractors in the 35–75hp range and commenced production. The company also signed an agreement with Flexi-Coil, a Canadian manufacturer of air seeding systems and tillage equipment. In Turkey, New Holland made a new agreement with its partner, KoÁ Group, increasing its share in the joint venture Türk Traktor to 37.5 per cent. New Holland Finance expanded its activities from the UK to other European markets, starting with Italy.

■ TOP *The 40 Series of New Holland tractors such as this model 7840 of 1996 can be considered state of the art, with its ergonomically designed cabs and modern four-wheel-drive systems.*

■ LEFT *A 1996 New Holland 7740 tractor from the 40 Series, with a New Holland 640 round baler in tow. The baler is capable of producing circular bales of up to 1.5m/5ft diameter.*

■ LEFT *A 1996 Ford New Holland four-wheel-drive 7840 Model tractor. Note the ballast weights at the front.*

■ ABOVE *A Ford New Holland 8340, one of the last to bear the Ford name.*

■ BELOW *New Holland still produces a range of towed harvesting implements including small rectangular balers, large square balers, and circular balers such as this Model 640.*

NUFFIELD

William Morris made his reputation as the force behind Morris cars, which became one of the British motor industry's most renowned names. As early as 1926 he had become interested in the tractor market and produced a small crawler tractor based on the track mechanism of a light tank. This project was later abandoned, but not forgotten, and work was progressing on another machine as the world moved towards the end of the war in the mid-1940s. A dozen prototypes were being tested in Lincolnshire by 1946 and, boosted by the success of these machines, plans for full-scale production at the Wolseley car factory were made. So Nuffield entered the tractor market with the Universal, which it unveiled at the 1948 Smithfield Agricultural Show.

The Universal was offered in two versions: the M4 was a four-wheeled

tractor and the M3 was a tricycle type for row crop work. The engine was derived from the wartime Morris Commercial engine, a four-cylinder side valve, and its tractor application was started on petrol and run on paraffin. It produced 42hp at 2000rpm. Later a diesel variant was offered, initially with a Perkins P4 unit, then later with a 3.4 litre British Motor Corporation (BMC) diesel following the Austin and Morris merger. In 1957 came the Universal 3, a three-cylinder diesel-engined tractor. The Universal 4/60 was announced in 1961. This was a 60hp tractor and the increased power had been achieved by boring out the existing 3.4 litre engine to 3.8 litres.

Production was eventually moved to the Bathgate plant in Scotland via the Morris Motors plant at Cowley in Oxfordshire. The Nuffield tractors were

■ RIGHT *A diesel version of the Nuffield M4. The engine was initially sourced from Perkins, then a 3.4 litre displacement British Motor Corporation diesel was used.*

■ BELOW *The early Nuffield M4 was regarded as a viable British alternative to imported American models. It had a five-speed transmission and a truck engine, and was noted for speed.*

■ BELOW *The 1949 M4 had a three-point linkage, drawbar and rear PTO drive.*

given a facelift in 1964 and became the 10–60 and 10–42 models. The tractors were redesigned for 1967, but before they could find widespread acceptance, Nuffield was involved in the merger that created the British Leyland Motor Corporation, making Nuffield tractors into Leylands. In 1981 Leyland was sold to the Nickerson organization.

NUFFIELD M4	
Year	1948
Engine	Morris Commercial ETA
Power	42hp at 2000rpm
Transmission	Five speed
Weight	n/k

OLIVER

Many of the major tractor manufacturing corporations were formed from the merger of numerous small companies, and Oliver is an example of this. In 1929, Hart-Parr, Nichols and Shepard and the American Seeding Machine Company all merged with the Oliver Chilled Plow Company to form the Oliver Farm Equipment Sales Company. The company then began to design a completely new line of tractors. Oliver itself dated back to 1855 and bore the name of its Scottish-born founder, James Oliver, who had developed a chilled steel plough. He had patented a process that gave the steel used in his ploughs a hard surface and tough consistency.

Once the Oliver Farm Equipment Sales Company was formed, the original Oliver company's prototype row crop models Models A and B could go into production. Oliver was the first company to use laterally adjustable rear wheels to suit the differing row spacings of different crops, but other manufacturers soon followed. These tractors were

■ ABOVE AND RIGHT *The Oliver Row Crop 60 made its debut in 1940 as a compact version of the already extant Row Crop 70.*

OLIVER 60 ROW CROP	
Year	1940
Engine	1894cc/115cu in
Power	n/k
Transmission	Four speed
Weight	907kg/2000lbs

■ BELOW *An Oliver Model 70 from 1937, by which time Oliver had dropped the Hart-Parr name.*

powered by a 18–27 four-cylinder engine that was also fitted to the company's line of conventional tractors, the Oliver Hart-Parr standard models. These were available in Standard, Western, Ricefield and Orchard versions and built until 1937. With a choice of four- or six-cylinder engines, these models became the Oliver 90 during the late 1930s. This was a three-speed 49hp machine.

■ **ROW CROP 70 HC**
The company achieved unexpected success with the Oliver Hart-Parr Row Crop 70 HC, which was introduced to the farming public in October 1935. This streamlined machine was fitted with a high compression, gasoline-fuelled, six-cylinder engine and was noted as being quiet and smooth running. By February 1936 Oliver had

sold in excess of 5000 examples, which was 3000 more than anticipated. An electric starter and lights were options.

In 1937 the Hart-Parr suffix was dropped from the company name so that the Model 70 Row Crop models carried only the Oliver name on their streamlined hoods. In the Nebraska Test the high-octane-fuelled, six-cylinder Row Crop 70 produced 22.64 drawbar hp and 28.37 belt hp. The Models 80 and 90 followed in 1938. The 80 had the angular look of earlier models while the 90 was run on kerosene. Oliver made both 90 and 99 Models between 1938 and 1952. After this date both were referred to as Model 99s. In 1940 the company introduced a smaller tractor, the 60, in a row crop config-uration and in 1944 it acquired Cletrac.

■ **FLEETLINE MODELS**
In 1948 Oliver unveiled a line of tractors to mark its 100th year in business. They were known as Fleetline Models 66, 77 and 88 and identified by a new grille and sheetmetal. Each was fitted with a power take-off and the range of engines offered something for every customer. Engine displacements ranged from the 2113cc/129cu in diesel to 3784cc/231cu in diesel installed in the 99 Model. Other diesel options in the new range included the 77 and 88

Models; otherwise the tractors used four-cylinder gasoline and paraffin engines. PTO equipment was standard but hydraulic lifts were not.

These models were followed by the Super Series of 44, 55, 66, 77, 88 and 99 Models. The Super 44 was the smallest model in the range, powered by a four-cylinder Continental L-head engine that was offset to permit the operator better visibility for field use. The Super 55 was a compact utility tractor which on gasoline produced 29.6 drawbar hp and 34.39 belt hp. Produc-tion of the Oliver 55 continued after Oliver was taken over by White. The Super 99 of 1954 was available with a

■ ABOVE LEFT *The Oliver 80 was another new model for 1940 although it did not have the streamlined styling of the 60 and 70 models.*

■ ABOVE RIGHT *The 80 was available with a gasoline engine, seen here, or one suited to running on kerosene distillate.*

three-cylinder, two-stroke, super-charged, General Motors diesel engine with a displacement of 3770cc/230cu in or an Oliver diesel. It was equipped with a three-point hitch and a cab was an extra-cost option.

In 1960 White Motor Corporation bought Oliver and later Cockshutt and Minneapolis-Moline. All eventually merged as White Farm Equipment.

■ LEFT *The Oliver 1955 model featured an angular cab, and was built during the 1970s, more than a decade after Oliver had been acquired by White. Both companies later became part of AGCO.*

RENAULT

In the early days of European tractor production France lagged behind the main European countries; tractor production was confined to the Renault Car Company although some Austin tractors were assembled in France. In the years immediately after World War I Renault (along with Peugeot and Citroën) announced the production of a crawler tractor. Renault's crawler was based on its experience of tank manufacture during the war. The tractor was subsequently designated the GP. It used a four-cylinder 30hp gasoline engine and a three-speed transmission with a single reverse gear; steering was by means of a tiller. An upgraded version, the H1, went on sale in 1920. Renault then developed the HO, a wheeled version of the H1. These models were powered by a four-cylinder engine that produced 20hp at 1600rpm and featured epicyclic reduction gears in the rear wheels. All these tractor models were based around a steel girder frame and the engine was enclosed

■ BELOW *The four-wheel-drive Renault Ceres 610RX, along with the smaller 85hp 95X, is part of a current range with a similar streamlined design.*

RENAULT 106.54 TRACTOR	
Year	1996
Engine	Six cylinder turbo diesel
Power	100hp, 75kW
Transmission	12 forward, 12 reverse
Weight	n/k

within a stylish curved bonnet (hood) that bore a close resemblance to Renault's trucks and cars of the time. The PE tractor was introduced in 1922 and was considerably redesigned from the earlier models. Renault introduced the VY tractor in 1933, powered by a 30hp in-line, four-cylinder diesel engine. It had a front-positioned radiator and the engine was enclosed. This model was painted yellow and grey and became the first diesel tractor to be produced in significant numbers in

■ RIGHT *Renault produces general tractors, such as this one seen ploughing in England, and specialist machines for orchard use.*

■ BELOW LEFT *A Renault tractor equipped with a French-manufactured hydraulic front loader.*

■ BELOW RIGHT *The Renault 106.54 is a four-wheel-drive 100hp tractor. The dual tyres and four-wheel drive help traction in heavy clay soils.*

France. Renault was also the major force in the World War II French tractor industry and had built in excess of 8500 tractors by 1948. Many of these were of the 303E model, although Renault followed this with the 3042 in 1948.

More recent tractors from Renault have included the Model 61 RS, a low-profile machine designed for operation in confined areas and powered by a three-cylinder diesel engine that makes 60hp and gives a maximum of 57hp at the PTO. The 80 TYX is a four-cylinder, water-cooled, diesel-powered tractor capable of producing 78hp. The Model 61 RS is available as either a two- or four-wheel-drive model with twelve forward and reverse gears. The Model 106.14 is a larger tractor with a six-cylinder diesel engine of 5656cc/345cu in displacement. It develops 96bhp and is available in both two- and four-wheel-drive configurations.

ROADLESS TRACTION LTD

In the UK, Roadless Traction Ltd of Hounslow designed numerous half-track bogie conversions for vehicles as diverse as a Foden steam lorry and a Morris Commercial. It later devised tracked conversions for various makes of tractor, including the Fordson E27N and forestry tractor conversions for Land Rover.

■ PHILIP JOHNSON

The company name Roadless Traction Ltd was registered on 4 March 1919 by Lieutenant Colonel Henry Johnson. Johnson was born in 1877 and attended the King Edward VII School in Birmingham before studying engineering at the Durham College of Science. After Durham he gained work experience in the heavy industries of South Wales before the outbreak of the Boer War in 1899. Johnson volunteered for the army, but was not selected because of defective eyesight, and found

his way to South Africa by working his passage on a cattle boat. Once in Cape Town he was able to get seconded to a steam road transport company of the Royal Engineers as a result of his experience with steam engines. The unit was responsible for towing howitzers and field guns as well as ammunition, mostly behind Fowler steam engines. It was here in South Africa that Johnson was able to study the use of mechanized transport in off-road situations. Johnson returned to England in 1906 and took up employment with the Leeds-based firm of Fowler and Compan. This required him to assist in the export of steam engines and involved a period of living in India. There Johnson is reputed to have delivered many Fowler engines under their own steam to the remotest parts of the sub-continent.

Johnson returned from India in 1915 to take up a wartime post with the Ministry of Munitions. He spent much of

those war years working on tank development and went out to France to the Front once the tanks were being used in combat. His tank development work, including that with rubber tracks and a spring and cable suspension system, continued after World War I.

Johnson's military duties ended in 1918 and during the 1920s he started converting Foden and Sentinel team lorries to half-tracks by substituting the driven rear wheels with tracks and bogies. It is estimated that the company invested £50,000 in the development of its products in the seven years following 1921. The company moved into Gunnersbury House, a former nunnery, in Hounslow, Middlesex in 1923. Johnson bought the house, leasing part to the company and living in the remainder.

Motor lorries of varying sizes were also converted to half-track in this period, including those from Peugeot,

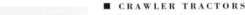

■ RIGHT *A 1941 Fordson N Roadless, equipped with a front-mounted, chain drive, Hesford winch.*

■ OPPOSITE BOTTOM *A Fordson Roadless half-track, in service with the Royal Air Force during World War II, towing a refuelling trailer. A group of WAAFs are refuelling a Hawker Hurricane.*

■ BELOW *A Fordson E27N converted to a half-track through the installation of Roadless DG4 tracks.*

Vulcan, Austin, Guy, Daimler, FWD and Morris Commercial. These were sold to customers in places as diverse as Scotland, Sudan and Peru. One of the company's first major commercially successful orders was for a batch of lorries for the Anglo-Persian Oil Company for use in connection with oil exploration in Iran. Roadless supplied converted Morris Commercial lorries to fulfil this order.

FORDSON N ROADLESS TRACTOR	
Year	1944
Engine	In-line four cylinder gasoline
Power	20hp
Transmission	Three speed
Weight	1225kg/2700lbs plus track bogies

■ CRAWLER TRACTORS

Following on from this growing success, the company turned its attention to tractors and potential agricultural applications for its technology. One of the first machines to be converted was the Peterbro tractor, manufactured by the Peter Brotherhood Ltd of Peterborough, Cambridgeshire.

This tractor used a four-cylinder gasoline-paraffin engine of Ricardo design that produced 30hp. Few of these tractors were made and even fewer – possibly only one – converted to half-track configuration using the Roadless components. Roadless also cooperated with another Peterborough-based firm, Barford and Perkins Ltd, to produce a half-track tractor. This was based on that company's THD road roller and powered by a rear-mounted, vertical, two-cylinder McLaren-Benz engine driving through a three-speed forward and reverse transmission. It utilized Roadless tracks and had a drawbar pull rated at 6858kg/ 17,419lb, but as it weighed 11 tons it was of limited use off-road and the project was abandoned.

The development of rubber-jointed tracks eventually enabled Roadless to produce viable agricultural machines. Its system, known as "E tracks", was easily adapted to many tractors and required little maintenance, so endearing it to farmers. The company converted AEC-manufactured Rushton tractors to full-tracks using E3 rubber-jointed tracks that were skid-steered, Ferodo-lined and differential-braked. Rushton Tractors was formed as a subsidiary of AEC in 1929 to manufacture Rushton and Roadless Rushton tractors. There were two variants of the Roadless Rushton with different lengths of track: the standard version had two rollers on each side while the other had three. These tractors were amongst those successfully demonstrated at the 1930 World Agricultural Tractor Trials held at Wallingford, Oxfordshire. The tractor was a success and sold in both the UK and export markets, although Rushton went out of business after an Algerian customer defaulted on payment for 100 tractors shipped there for use in vineyards.

The Fordson tractor was gaining in popularity and in 1929 the first

■ ABOVE *This 1950 Roadless Model E is powered by a TVO engine. It is thought that a total of only 25 machines were ever made.*

ROADLESS FULL-TRACK MODEL E	
Year	1950
Engine	Fordson TVO or diesel option
Power	40hp
Transmission	Three speed
Weight	n/k

Roadless conversion on a Fordson tractor was carried out on a Fordson Model N. It was successfully demonstrated on Margate Beach early in 1930, when it hauled 3 tons of seaweed off the beach. Roadless-converted Fordsons soon became popular and were offered in two track lengths. Fordson tractor production was moved from Ireland to Dagenham in 1931 and Fordson approved the conversion for use with its machines. The association

between Ford and Roadless Traction would endure from then until the 1980s.

Another major tractor maker to take advantage of Roadless crawler technology was Case of Racine, Wisconsin. A number of Case tractors, including the Models C, L and LH, were converted and, unlike the other conversions, the Case tractors retained their steering wheels. Roadless built experimental machines for McLaren, Lanz, Bolinder-Munktell, Mavag and Allis-Chalmers, although many never progressed beyond prototypes. Forestry and lifeboat hauling were two tasks that were ideally suited to the Roadless converted machines.

The war years saw Roadless building a variety of machines for the British Air Ministry to use as aircraft tugs. Despite being almost blitzed out of its factory, the company's production was entirely devoted to war requirements, whether it was experimental work or track conversions to imported American tractors from manufacturers such as Case, Massey-Harris and Oliver.

In the immediate post-war years

Roadless converted a large number of the popular Fordson E27N tractors, that were sold through advertisements in many Ford publications. The conversion received an accolade when it was awarded a silver medal at the 1948 Royal Show in York. Subsequently several versions of the E27N were built and exported widely.

Through the 1950s the company diversified, turning its attention to full-track and four-wheel-drive tractors. This and its connections with the forestry industry would ultimately lead to the Roadless-converted Land Rover. In the same way as the company's half-tracks were built by converting wheeled tractors, so too were the full-track models. The Fordson Model E was converted and later the Fordson Diesel Major was converted as the Roadless J17. At the same time the company also developed a row crop tricycle conversion for the Fordson E27N Major for sale in the United States and this stayed in production until 1964.

The first Roadless 4×4 Tractor appeared in 1956, overseen by Philip Johnson who was now running the company. He travelled widely to see his company's products in use. While in Italy to visit Landini he met Dr Segre-Amar who had founded the Selene company, based near Turin. Selene converted Fordson tractors to 4×4 configuration using a transfer box and war surplus GMC 6×6 truck front axles. A working relationship between the two men developed that ultimately led to the Roadless company producing the 4×4 Fordsons in Britain. This tractor was a great success and subsequently Roadless converted the Power Major of 1958 and the later Super Major in large numbers, together with a small batch of Fordson Dextas. International Harvester also marketed a Roadless converted 4×4 tractor known as the B-450, that was constructed in International's Doncaster factory in England. It stayed in production until 1970.

■ **ROADLESS ROVERS**

Around the end of the 1950s the Hounslow company focused its attention on the light 4×4 Land Rover which had now been in production for a decade. The Forestry Commission was experiencing some difficulty with its use of conventional Land Rovers, which were prone to getting stuck on rutted forest tracks and were hampered by fallen trees in cross-country use. The Machinery Research Officer for the Forestry Commission, Colonel Shaw, suggested that tractor-type 25 × 70cm/ 10 × 28in wheels should be fitted to the Land Rover. A prototype was built and evaluated in the Alice Holt Forest in Hampshire, England. The verdict was that the machine had potential but required further development in order to be viable. A 2.77m/109in wheelbase Land Rover was despatched to the Hounslow premises of Roadless for a redesigned and properly engineered conversion to be effected.

Roadless used a combination of components to make the machine functional: it retained the original gear- and transfer boxes and coupled them to a pair of Studebaker axles with GKN-Kirkstall planetary hub reductions and the same 25 × 70cm/10 × 28in wheels that had been used before. The front axle had a track 35cm/14in wider than the rear in order to facilitate sufficient steering lock to retain the vehicle's manoeuvrability. The turning circle was approximately 12m/40ft. In order to accommodate the large wheels and tyres the normal Land Rover front wings (fenders) were removed and replaced with huge flat wings while the rear ones were fabricated in the manner of tractor rear wheel arches. With the change in gear ratios and wheel diameter the complete machine was capable of approximately 48kph/30mph.

This machine was despatched to the Forestry Commission's test site at the Alice Holt Forest. Roadless prepared a second prototype that was sent to the Special Projects Department of the Rover Co Ltd. It was thoroughly tested – reportedly at the Motor Industry Research Association (MIRA) cross-country course at Lindley. Roadless made some further modifications to the Land Rover, including strengthening the chassis and altering the axle clearances, and after a couple of years of tests Rover approved the conversion. This approval meant that the converted Land Rover could be marketed as the Roadless 109 from 1961. In December of the same

year the 2286cc/139cu in gasoline engine model retailed at £1558 and the diesel variant at £1658. A special pick-up body was listed as an extra at £172. The Roadless was capable of returning 35kpg/10mpg and had a 68 litre/15 gallon tank. Tests showed that the machine understeered when cornering at 24kph/15mph, the steering was heavy at low speeds and that the machine was capable of wading in up to 75cm/2½ft of water. This latter fact was one of the features that Roadless Traction Ltd mentioned in its advertisements, also pointing out that the wide track ensured stability on side slopes – a useful asset

for forestry work. The Land Rover project was something of a side-show for Roadless, as by the mid-1960s the major portion of its business was the production of four-wheel-drive tractors. Approximately 3000 Roadless four-wheel-drive Fordson tractors had been manufactured when production of the Fordson Super Major ended in 1964.

■ **ROADLESS 4X4s**

Over the next decade things would change considerably for the company. The first major change was brought about by the death of Lieutenant Colonel Philip Johnson on 8 November 1965 at the age of 88. Johnson had been active in Roadless right into his last years and had only relinquished the managing director's post in 1962. His death meant that a reshuffle took place. Four-wheel-drive tractor production continued, with Roadless conversions being supplied for Ford's new range of 2000, 3000, 4000 and 5000 tractors. The 5000 was the most powerful, a 65hp unit with a choice of eight- or ten-speed transmissions and in Roadless converted form known as the Ploughmaster 65, still using a GMC front axle. This was followed by the Ploughmaster 95.

These tractors, like their predecessors, had smaller front wheels than rear ones but the technology employed in the Land Rover had taught lessons, because in the mid-1960s the company had drawn up plans for four-wheel-drive tractor conversions that had equal-sized wheels all round, like the Roadless 109. The Roadless 115 was one of the first tractors of this design to be produced.

Successful demonstrations of Roadless' products at the Long Sutton Tractor Trials in Lincolnshire meant that through the 1970s the company was not short of work. Increasingly stringent legislation affected Roadless' tractors, and from the end of the 1970s the company was required to fit its machines with "Quiet Cabs".

In 1979 the company relocated from its original premises in Hounslow to Sawbridgeworth in Hertfordshire,

England. Sales of Roadless 4×4 tractors had started to slacken simply because of increasing competition from other 4×4 tractor makers, including cheaper machines from Same, Belarus and Zetor from Eastern Europe, as well as machines from the other international major tractor makers.

Roadless then diversified into the manufacture of log-handling machinery and forestry tractors, but with hindsight it appears that Roadless had had its day. A combination of circumstances and the recession of the early 1980s forced the companies that made up Roadless into voluntary liquidation.

ROADLESS 109 LAND ROVER

Year	1961
Engine	In-line four cylinder diesel
Power	67bhp (50kW) @ 4000rpm
Transmission	Eight forward, two reverse
Weight	3052kg/6728lbs

■ TOP AND LEFT *The Roadless Traction conversion was made to the 109in wheelbase Land Rover models. This is a diesel-powered Series II version, and the conversion was aimed at forestry work. The conversion involved swapping both the front and rear axles for Studebaker ones that increased ground clearance and track.*

OTHER MAKES

(Same, Somua, Steyr)

■ SAME

Same is an Italian company that was founded in 1942 and currently owns the Lamborghini brand. One of the company's earliest tractors was the 4R20M of 1950 which was powered by a 2hp, twin-cylinder, gasoline and kerosene engine. Same production included the Condor 55 and Models 90 and 100 of the mid-1980s. The Condor 55 is a conventional tractor powered by a 2827cc/172.4cu in 1003P, direct-injection, air-cooled diesel with three cylinders that produces 55hp. The 90 and 100 Models are from a range where the numerical designation approximates to the number of horsepower that they produce. Each has 12 forward and three reverse gears and can achieve 30kph/19mph. Both have two-speed power take-off and hydrostatic steering.

■ LEFT *Same was founded by Francesco Cassani in 1942. This is a Same Antares 100 from 1990.*

■ BELOW *The Same Silver 90 of 1995 is a four-wheel-drive tractor from a range of similar tractors with different outputs.*

■ ABOVE *Same now builds machines such as the 130 Antares and is noted for 4x4 tractors.*

■ BELOW *The Same Silver 90 has a turbo diesel engine that produces in the region of 90hp.*

■ RIGHT *Somua was one of the numerous French manufacturers that produced agricultural tractors in the inter-war decades. This one is working at Courtelin, France.*

■ SOMUA

Somua was a French manufacturer of agricultural machinery in the inter-war years and among its products was a machine with a rear, power-driven rotary cultivator. Other French makes of similar machines included Amiot and Dubois. The former was a machine with an integral plough while the latter was a reversible motor plough.

■ STEYR

The Austrian manufacturer Steyr entered the tractor market in 1928 when it announced an 80hp machine of which only a few were made. After World War II Steyr returned to tractor manufacture with the Model 180, a two-cylinder diesel, in 1948 and the smaller Model 80 in 1949. These were followed during the 1950s by the models 185 and 280, three- and four-cylinder diesel tractors respectively. The company was based in St Valentin, Austria and through the 1980s and 1990s offered a range of row crop and utility tractors ranging from 42 to 145hp.

In 1996 the Case Corporation acquired 75 per cent of the shares in Steyr Landmaschinentechnik GmbH (SLT) from Steyr-Daimler-Puch AG.

■ LEFT *An earlier Somua tractor in use on the Normandy coast of France for transporting fishing boats from the water across the long, sloping beach.*

■ LEFT *Austrian Steyr resumed tractor manufacture after World War II, and has manufactured tractors ever since. This is a modern, four-wheel-drive example of the company's products.*

STEIGER

The first Steiger tractor was built in
North Dakota in the late 1950s. Named
after the brothers who designed it, this
tractor is reputed to have gone on to
achieve more than 10,000 hours of field
time and is now on display in the
museum at Bonanzaville in West Fargo,
North Dakota. The first Steiger
manufacturing plant was a dairy barn on
the Steiger brothers' farm near Thief
River Falls in Minnesota. By the late
1960s, the company had been
incorporated and moved into larger
facilities in Fargo. Several moves and
several years later, Steiger tractor
manufacturing arrived at its current
Fargo location. The distinctive lime-
green Steiger tractors were constructed
around engines that produced up to
525hp. The tractors were named after
animals including Puma, Bearcat,
Cougar, Panther, Lion and Tiger, and
each name denoted a specific
horsepower class.

In 1986, Steiger was acquired by
Case IH. To consolidate the merger, both
companies' four-wheel-drive tractor

■ LEFT *Steiger
tractors were
finished in a
distinctive shade of
lime green, and
named after
animals. This
Cougar II is one
such tractor.*

■ ABOVE *Steiger built large tractors for
other manufacturers including this, the Allis
Chalmers 440 of 1973, which was followed
by the 4W-305 of 1986.*

lines were unified in both colour and
name. The name Steiger was associated
with high-power tractors and in a survey
of farmers in four-wheel-drive tractor
markets, this name was cited as the
most popular and well-known four-
wheel-drive tractor brand. As a result
the name was later revived for the Case
IH 9300 Series tractors which were
then claimed to be the industry's
leading line of four-wheel-drive
machines. For a period a Hungarian
tractor-making company produced
RABA-Steiger tractors under licence
from the Steiger company.

The current range, the 9300 Series of
massive four-wheel-drive tractors from
Case IH, consists of a range of ten

■ ABOVE *This 1992 Steiger Case IH 9280
is fitted with triple tyres and has been
specifically designed for the needs of the
large acreage farmer.*

■ LEFT *Case IH acquired Steiger in 1986.
Following the merger both companies'
tractors bore the red and grey of Case IH.
This 9280 model dates from 1992.*

STEIGER 9310 4WD TRACTOR	
Year	1996
Engine	Case 6TA, six cylinder
Power	207 PTO hp, 240 bhp
Transmission	12 forward, three reverse
Weight	9537kg/21,026lbs

Steiger machines. The models range from 240 to 425hp, with two row crop special models and the Quadtrac tractor which features four independent crawler tracks. The current 9300 Series tractors are designed and manufactured in Fargo, North Dakota.

Four-wheel-drive tractors have the perceived advantage of superior flotation compared to two-wheel-drive tractors. Weight and pull are evenly distributed with less slippage, less rolling resistance and more drawbar pull. The 9300 Steiger tractors offer fuel efficiency through the use of the

■ ABOVE *The diesel-powered Steiger ST-310 Panther has a Cummins engine, as does the larger Tiger ST-470.*

■ BELOW *The Steiger Panther ST-310 has a 855cu in displacement, six-cylinder, diesel engine, which produces 310bhp.*

Case 8.3 L, Cummins N14 and Cummins M11 engines. These have been engineered to provide the optimum balance of torque rise, power curve and fuel economy. The 9300 Series models range from the 240hp 9330 to the 425hp 9390. The optional transmissions are as follows: a 12-speed SynchroShift standard, a 24-speed hi-low SynchroShift and a 12-speed full Powershift, although not all these transmissions are available on all models. This series of tractors is comprehensively equipped in terms of hitches, hydraulics and power take-offs. Lift capacities range from 6662–8884kg/14,689–19,586lb, depending on the model.

OTHER MAKES

(Tung Fung Hung, Twin City, Universal,
Ursus, Valmet, Versatile, Volvo,
Waterloo Boy)

■ TUNG FUNG HUNG

Tractor production has always had a place
in Chinese agriculture despite the
availability of a huge pool of labour. Tung
Fung Hung is one of several Chinese
manufacturers. During the 1950s the
company built a tractor known as the Iron
Buffalo and a crawler in state factories. It
also built a version of the MTZ tractor from
the Minsk Tractor Works. A number of
Chinese factories produce tractors for
export, and these machines are marketed
under a variety of other names, such as
American Harvester.

■ ABOVE *Both conventional tractors and crawlers have
been widely built in China.*

■ TOP *In China
agriculture is
not as reliant on
technology as in
other parts of
the world,
although
compact tractors
such as this
machine in
Nanking are
widely used.*

■ ABOVE *Small
farm machines,
such as this in
the Hunan
Province of
China, rely on
small engines
with tractor-
type tyres.*

■ ABOVE *A machine in the Yixing Province
of China used for a plethora of tasks.*

■ RIGHT *Over the years the Universal name has been used by a variety of tractor makers both as a brand and a model designation. This is a UTB Universal 530.*

■ TWIN CITY

Twin City was the brand name used by the Minneapolis Steel and Machinery Company which produced tractors for a time. In 1910 it introduced the Twin City 40. Its steam engine influences were obvious: it had an exposed engine in place of the boiler, a cylindrical radiator and a long roof canopy. The Twin City 40 was powered by an in-line four-cylinder engine and its larger cousin the 60–90 by an in-line six-cylinder of massive displacement. The 90 suffix indicated 90hp at 500rpm. The machine also had 2.1m/7ft diameter rear wheels and a single speed transmission which made it capable of 3kph/2mph. In 1929 Minneapolis Steel and Machinery became part of Minneapolis-Moline.

■ UNIVERSAL

In 1915 the Moline Plow Company purchased the Universal Tractor Company of Columbus, Ohio. The product line was moved to Moline, Illinois and a new building was built for the production of the Moline Universal Tractor. The Moline Universal Tractor was a two-wheel unit design for use with the farmer's horse-drawn implements as well as newly developed Moline tractor-drawn implements. It was commonly referred to as the first row crop tractor, and was equipped with electric lights and a starter, which was very advanced for its time.

■ ABOVE *The UTB Universal 600 is a diesel-engined tractor made in Brasov, Romania, where production started in 1946. Like other Eastern Bloc tractor makers UTB considered exports important.*

■ LEFT *The UTB logo indicates that the 600 model, seen here at a European vintage machinery rally, was made by Universal Tractors of Brasov.*

OTHER MAKES

■ ABOVE *Ursus tractor manufacture started in Poland, with a design based on that of the Lanz Bulldog, and then a standardized Eastern Bloc tractor. This much later 106-14 is working in Ireland.*

■ LEFT *An Ursus tractor, photographed in the Kielce province of Poland. Exports of Ursus tractors were made to the United States as well as much of Europe.*

■ OPPOSITE TOP *The Valmet 8450 is a modern, four-wheel-drive tractor, powered by a 140hp turbocharged diesel engine.*

■ OPPOSITE *Canadian company Versatile offered massive articulated tractors from 1966 onwards. The 895 is a 310hp 14,010cc/855cu in displacement machine that articulates behind the cab.*

■ UNIVERSAL

Another company to use the Universal brand name was a Romanian company based in Brasov. They began production in 1946 and exported widely. A mid-1980s product was the Model 1010 which is powered by a 100hp 5393cc/329cu in six-cylinder diesel engine. In the United States the Romanian Universal tractors are marketed under the Long brand name.

■ URSUS

Ursus was a state-owned Polish tractor maker whose tractors were very similar to those from other State-owned companies elsewhere in the Eastern Bloc including 1950s models from the East German (DDR) ZT concern and Czechoslovakian Zetor. Tractors were also produced in Bulgaria under the Bolgar name.

■ VALMET

Valmet is a Finnish tractor maker which was amalgamated with Volvo BM from Sweden in 1972. The company has specialized in forestry tractors such as

the Jehu 1122. This machine is a wheeled tractor although provision has been made to install tracks over the tyres to improve traction in deep snow. Volvo BM Valmet also made the 2105, a 163hp six-cylinder, turbo diesel tractor as part of a range.

■ VERSATILE

In 1947 the Hydraulic Engineering Company was formed in Toronto, Canada and began production of small-size agricultural implements under the Versatile name. In 1954 the Hydraulic Engineering Company launched its first large machine,

OTHER MAKES

an innovative self-propelled swather. The Hydraulic Engineering Company was incorporated in 1963 as a public company, adopting the name Versatile Manufacturing Ltd. Then in 1966 Versatile, operating out of Winnipeg, Canada, became involved in the manufacture of huge four-wheel-drive tractors that produced power in excess of 200hp. Versatile Manufacturing Ltd changed ownership in 1976 and changed names in 1977, becoming the Versatile Farm Equipment Company, a division of Versatile Corporation. In 1991 the Versatile Farm Equipment Company became part of Ford New Holland Americas, N. H. Geotech's United States division.

■ **VOLVO**

The Sweden based Volvo group is a massive motor manufacturer and a long-established tractor maker. During the 1920s it produced tractors alongside Munktells who it later acquired.

Volvo tractors have a history of diesel engine fitment: during the 1950s the T30 model used a Perkins L4 engine, for example. Another Scandinavian merger occurred in 1972 when Volvo began to cooperate with Finnish Valmet in the manufacture of tractors, offering the Nordic range specifically designed for Scandinavian countries. During the 1980s Volvo manufactured the 805 model in two forms: the 805 was a two-wheel-drive tractor, while the 805-4 was a four-wheel-drive variant. Both were powered by a 95hp four-cylinder turbocharged diesel engine. A larger tractor from the same era was the 2105 model. Volvo was among the first to design and fit safety cabs to its tractors. Its machines have been exported widely around Europe and to the United States.

■ LEFT *Versatile is a Canadian tractor maker who from the early 1970s specialized in the production of large four-wheel-drive tractors such as the 895.*

■ BELOW *In 1991 Versatile became part of Ford New Holland which led to machines such as the articulated four-wheel-drive 946 model being produced in Ford's blue colours.*

The company took a renewed interest in tractors in 1911 and by 1914 had produced the forerunner of what became the Model R. It was powered by a horizontal two-cylinder engine and soon superseded by the Model N. This went on sale in 1916 and over its eight-year production run, around 20,000 were made. The Waterloo Boy Model N was sold in Britain as the Overtime by the Overtime Farm Tractor Company, based in London. The Model N had a massive chassis frame on which was mounted the fuel tank, radiator, twin-cylinder engine and driver's seat. The engine, which was started with petrol and then run on paraffin, produced 25hp. The use of roller bearings throughout the machine was considered innovative at the time of its manufacture.

This early tractor had differing but equally important influences on two other tractor companies. The Belfast agent for Overtime Tractors was Harry Ferguson: this was his first experience with tractors and started him thinking of better ways of attaching implements. It was also the Waterloo Boy that brought John Deere into the tractor business. In 1918 Deere and Company bought the Waterloo Gasoline Engine Company for $1 million and initially kept the Model N in production as a John Deere tractor.

■ WATERLOO BOY

John Froelich built a machine powered by a Van Duzen single-cylinder engine in Iowa that many consider as the first practical tractor. The engine of the machine was mounted on the Robinson chassis from a steam engine and Froelich devised a transmission system. He was experienced in the agricultural business and had worked as a threshing contractor, so was aware of the requirements of mechanized harvesting.

Froelich bought a large Case thresher and transported it together with a wagon for the crew to live in, by rail to Langford, South Dakota. It is reported that hundreds turned out to see the machines at work, as over a seven-week period his crew threshed wheat full time. His machinery suffered no breakdowns and as a result many were convinced of the benefits of mechanization. As a result Froelich gained backing from a group of Iowa businessmen and they formed the Waterloo Gasoline Traction Engine Company. In 1893 the company built four more tractors, of which only two were fully workable, and others in 1896 and 1897. The company dropped the word "Traction" from its name in 1895 and concentrated on the manufacture of stationary engines. John Froelich's interest was primarily in tractors so he left the company at this time.

■ ABOVE *A Volvo BM Valmet 405 tractor. Its maker's name carries the heritage of Volvo, Bolinder, Munktell and Valmet.*

■ ABOVE *The Waterloo Boy Model N kerosene tractor, the machine that brought John Deere into tractor manufacture.*

WHITE FARM EQUIPMENT

The White Motor Corporation of Cleveland, Ohio became established in the tractor manufacturing industry during the early 1960s when the corporation bought up a number of relatively small tractor-producing companies. These companies were, in the main, established concerns with a long history of involvement in the tractor industry, often going back to its earliest days. In 1960 White bought Oliver but continued to produce the successful and popular Oliver 55 Models throughout the decade. Oliver had been in business since 1929 when it, too, had come about as a result of combining several small companies.

White purchased the Cockshutt Farm Equipment Company in 1962. This company's history stretched back to 1839. In more recent times Cockshutt manufactured tractors such as the Models 20 and 40. The 20 was introduced in 1952 and used a Continental L-head 2294cc/140cu in, four-cylinder engine and a four-speed transmission. The Model 40 was a six-cylinder, six-speed tractor. Following these acquisitions, White acquired

■ LEFT *Cockshutt was a long-established tractor maker and was acquired by the White Motor Corporation in 1962, after White had acquired Oliver and before it acquired Minneapolis-Moline.*

Minneapolis-Moline a year later. The brand names of all three companies were retained by White until as late as 1969, when the entire company was restructured as White Farm Equipment. During the 1970s White produced a tractor named the Plainsman. This was an eight-wheeler powered by an 8260cc/504cu in displacement engine that produced 169hp. Subsequently, White was itself acquired. A company based in Dallas, Texas, the TIC Investment Corporation, bought White Farm Equipment in 1981 and continued its business under the acronym WFE.

The Allied Products Corporation of Chicago bought parts of WFE including the Charles City, Iowa tractor plant and stock. In 1987 Allied combined White with the New Idea Farm Equipment Company, forming a new division known as White-New Idea. In 1993 the AGCO Corporation of Waycross, Georgia purchased the White-New Idea range of implements, and has retained the White name for its brand of tractors. The current White tractor models range from 45 to 215hp, and include proprietary systems, such as Synchro-Reverser, Powershift and Quadrashift

■ ABOVE *The White 2-60 Field Boss was marketed as a White tractor during the latter part of the 1970s.*

■ LEFT *The 4-150 Field Boss was one of the large tractors made by White Farm Equipment.*

■ LEFT *This Model
60 White tractor
was made in 1989
when the company
was under the
control of the
Allied Products
Corporation of
Chicago.*

transmissions. They are powered by
Cummins direct-injected diesels. The
range includes the following models:
6045 and 6065 Mid-Size, 6090 Hi-
Clearance, six Fieldmaster and three
Powershift models.

■ WHITE 6045

The 45 PTO hp 6045 Mid-Size has a 50
degree turning angle and there is a
choice of two-wheel-drive or a model
with a driven front axle. The Synchro-
Reverser transmission has twelve gears
in forward and reverse. The 6065 Mid-
Size develops 63hp at the PTO and has
a 12 speed Synchro-Reverser
transmission and a four-cylinder engine.
Both two- and four-wheel-drive models
are available. The 6090 Hi-Clearance
tractor is an 80 PTO hp tractor with
generous ground clearance. It gives
69cm/27.2in of crop clearance and
59cm/23.2in of ground clearance under
the front and rear axles as well as

WHITE 8410 4WD TRACTOR	
Year	1998
Engine	Cummins B5.9 six cylinder
Power	145 PTO hp
Transmission	32 forward, 32 reverse
Weight	7303kg/16,110lbs

■ BELOW *The White A4T Plainsman of
1971 was a large articulated tractor with a
8260cc/504cu in displacement engine.*

55cm/21.7in of ground clearance under
the drawbar. The 6090 in this form has
a synchromesh transmission with 20
forward and 20 reverse gears as standard.
The 6175 and 6195 Powershift Series
ranges from 124–200 PTO hp and offers
an electronically controlled full powershift transmission. It has 18 forward and
nine reverse gears. The White 6215
Powershift has 215 PTO hp and a
Powershift transmission with 18 forward
and nine reverse gears. It is powered by
a Cummins 6-cylinder, 8300cc/506cu in
displacement, turbo-charged,
aftercooled engine.

OTHER MAKES

■ WIKOV

In the mid-1920s, in a Czechoslovakia recently independent from
the Austro-Hungarian Empire, the
two-cylinder Wikov 22 was made by
Wichterie and Kovarik of Prostejov.
Other noted Czechoslovakian motor
manufacturers who offered tractors
were Praga and Skoda, whose
constituent companies had previously
offered motor ploughs.

Praga offered the AT25, KT32 and
U50 models while Skoda offered a
four-cylinder powered, three-speed
tractor designated the 30HT. It could
be run on either kerosene or a mixture
of alcohol and gasoline which was
known as "Dynalkol".

ZETOR

The Zetor tractor company was established in 1946 in Brno, Czech Republic, and became one of the largest European tractor manufacturers. More than half a million Zetor tractors have been produced and have been sold in over 100 countries around the world. Zetor tractors are marketed and currently sold worldwide through two major distribution channels. The first of these is the companies of the Motokov Group, with offices around the world, while the second is the John Deere dealer network. This was made possible through long-term marketing agreements reached between the Motokov Group, John Deere and Zetor. Zetor tractors have been sold in the United States since 1982 and in 1984 American Jawa Ltd took over the distribution. Zetor tractors are distributed in America through two major service and distribution centres, one in Harrisburg, Pennsylvania and the other in La Porte, Texas. In 1993, under a distribution agreement reached with John Deere,

Zetor was able to distribute a lower-priced line of 40–85hp tractors in what are considered to be emerging markets, starting with selected areas of Latin America and Asia.

Zetor designs and manufactures most of its own tractor components, including the engines that are designed to be fuel-efficient. Throughout its history Zetor has endeavoured to pioneer various innovations. It had one of the first hitch hydraulic systems, known as Zetormatic, which it introduced in 1960. Later, Zetor was the among the first tractor

■ ABOVE *A Zetor tractor exported to England and fitted with the Zetormatic hitch system, a hydraulic system for hitching implements such as this hay rake.*

■ LEFT *Zetor has always seen exports as an important part of its business. This 1970s model is in France but the company has exported to more than 100 countries worldwide.*

■ ABOVE *The Zetor 25 was a 25hp tractor with a two-cylinder diesel engine, introduced in 1945, and one of the earliest Zetor tractors to be exported from the Czech Republic.*

■ BOTTOM *The 1966 Zetor 3011 Diesel tractor was wholly conventional. The steering arm runs alongside the engine to the front axle.*

■ BELOW *For a time Zetor tractors, Polish Ursus tractors and ZT tractors from East Germany were almost identical, as the result of Soviet control.*

■ BELOW *This Zetor 3011 diesel tractor was manufactured in Zetor's Brno, Czechoslovakia plant and exported to Britain, although others went to Ireland and as far as New Zealand in the 1950s.*

companies to manufacture fully integrated safety cabs with insulated, rubber-mounted suspension. The Zetor 8045 Crystal Model of 1986 had an engine of 4562cc/278cu in displacement and used diesel fuel. It produced power in the region of 85hp. It is a 4×4 tractor with 8 forward gears and two reverse. In 1997 the Zetor product line included ten different tractors. These ranged from the 46hp Models 3320 and 3340 to the 90hp Models 9640 and 10540. While Zetor is a Czechoslovakian company, versions of its tractors are assembled in numerous countries around the world including Argentina, Burma, India, Iraq, Uruguay and Zaire.

ZETOR 8045 CRYSTAL	
Year	1986
Engine	4562cc/278cu in in-line four cylinder diesel
Power	85hp
Transmission	Eight forward, two reverse gears
Weight	n/k

FARMING IMPLEMENTS

The versatility of tractors is enhanced through the use of specialist implements designed for specific farming tasks, both for preparing the land and harvesting the crop. The implements are generally one of two types: those that are attached to the tractor and those that are towed behind it.

In some farming areas the soil can be too wet for the propagation of crops so machines that drain fields are used as well as machines capable of working in wet and heavy soils without becoming bogged down. Draining the fields can sometimes be achieved through the use of a mole plough which cuts narrow drainage channels into the surface of a field, allowing a network of such channels to carry away excess water. More recently machines have been developed that lay lengths of perforated plastic pipe that drains fields.

Maintenance of hedges is quickly achieved through the use of hedge trimmers while the quality of fields is upgraded through the application of

■ LEFT *Tractors such as this Farmall Row Crop model are designed for use in the cultivation of crops, and pass through fields with minimum damage to a growing crop.*

■ ABOVE *Four-wheel-drive tractors such as this Massey Ferguson offer sufficient traction to enable them to pull implements such as rippers and sub-soilers as here.*

■ LEFT *Modern tractors are often equipped with implements to the front and rear to maximize produc-tivity by combining several sowing tasks into a single-pass operation.*

■ RIGHT *A four-wheel-drive John Deere tractor with a seed drill being towed by the tractor and powered by its PTO. The drill delivers metered amounts of seed and fertilizer.*

■ BELOW RIGHT *Ploughing remains one of the timeless farming tasks for which tractors are essential.*

various chemical fertilizers in both powder and liquid form, and implements exist for the distribution of these fertilizers as well as the more traditional use of manure.

While ploughs are now more massive and complex than they have ever been, the concept of ploughing remains unchanged. The purpose of ploughing is to break up the top layer of soil in order to allow the roots of growing plants to penetrate the soil. Ploughs are designed to slice into the top layer and, through the curve of the mouldboard, invert it. John Deere's contribution to ploughing with the development of the self-scouring steel plough suitable for heavy

■ ABOVE *The hydraulic front loader is a versatile farming implement, especially when it can be fitted with a variety of tools as on this John Deere.*

■ RIGHT *A John Deere ploughing. The plough is attached to the tractor's three-point hitch and is adjustable to take into account soil conditions.*

■ ABOVE *John Deere is a manufacturer of a full line of tractors and implements incluidng tandem disc harrows such as this 235 model.*

■ BELOW *John Deere's air seeding system is a complex, efficient system of planting that makes sowing a one-pass operation, opening, seeding and closing as it goes.*

prairie soils cannot be overestimated. Ploughs are manufactured around the world by specialists such as Ransomes in the UK, Kverneland in Norway, both Niemeyer and Krone in Germany as well as the major full-line manufacturers such as John Deere, Massey-Ferguson and constituent parts of the AGCO Corporation. Cultivators are a vital part of preparing the land after ploughing and these are made by a similar range of companies. Rotary power harrows, soil packers, sub-tillers, tine cultivators and rollers are all specialized implements for dealing with a variety of field conditions.

Seeding is just as mechanized a process as ploughing and massive seed drills made by the likes of John Deere illustrate how far mechanization has come since Jethro Tull devised his seed drill. Despite this the machines still carry out the same task, namely that of depositing the seeds below the surface of the soil where they will germinate. Once the seeds are planted by means of

■ RIGHT *A John
Deere planter
behind a John
Deere tractor. To
enable such large
implements to be
transported to
fields they are
designed to fold up
behind the tractor.*

a broadcaster or the increasingly
popular seed drill, the farmer is likely to
spray fertilizer and pesticides. The
implements (and tractors) for this must
pass through and over the crop with
minimal damage, which has led to
numerous high-clearance machines
being devised and, of course, the row
crop tractor. Drills and planters are
made by the full-line manufacturers and
specialists such as Smallford, Reekie
and Hestair in the UK, and the likes of
Vaderstad, Kuhn and Westmac in

■ LEFT *A John
Deere rotary disk
mower, designed
for cutting grass
and hay.*

■ BELOW *Planting
is increasingly
scientific, with
tools controlling
the depth at which
the seed is planted
and adding precise
amounts of
fertilizer.*

■ LEFT *The hay rake such as this, seen in England behind a Fergy TE2,0 was used to turn the mown grass to allow it to dry before being baled.*

■ BELOW *This vintage haymaking equipment indicates how the harvest is more precisely managed now.*

■ BOTTOM *A twin axle trailer, behind an International Harvester tractor, being used to carry away grain.*

Europe. Sprayers are produced by a considerable number of companies including Hardi, Vicon, ETS Matrot and Moteska.

Once the growing cycle is completed another array of specialist harvesting machinery is used. Apart from combine harvesters for grain and balers for hay there are specific harvesters for crops that include peas, beans, beet, cotton, sugar cane, root vegetables and tobacco. Geography and climate mean that some of these machines are specific to certain parts of the world. Massey-Ferguson, Claas, Deutz-Fahr, New Holland and John Deere are among the noted manufacturers of combines worldwide. In addition to self-propelled harvesting machines there are a considerable variety designed to be towed behind tractors. One of the largest groups of these are mowers and rotary rakes, both of which are used for haymaking. In recent years balers have been developed considerably and towed balers are now capable of producing much larger hay bales than previously. Some of the new generation of balers produce large circular bales which pose their own problems of handling and storage, and specific loaders have been devised for this. Forage harvesters are also available in both self-propelled and towed implement forms for the harvesting of grass and for silage making.

The scientific approach to farming has led to the development of specialized loading and handling machinery including the rough-terrain fork lift and the loader. The hydraulic front loader was one of the first machines of this type, although the capabilities of even these have been increased in recent years. John Deere currently manufactures a range of tools for hydraulic loaders that include various sizes of bucket, a bale hugger, a pallet fork, a round bale fork and a bale and silage grapple.

■ RIGHT *Self-propelled aquatic harvesters are particularly specialized implements, designed for marine plants and weed beds.*

■ ABOVE LEFT *The shift to round bales led to the development of a spike tool for handling the bales, to be fitted to hydraulic loaders.*

■ ABOVE RIGHT *This photograph from the late 1960s shows square bales being taken by trailer from the fields where they have been harvested to storage in a barn.*

■ RIGHT *A small Fendt Dieselross tractor equipped with a sidebar mower.*

INDEX

NOTES

NOTES

NOTES

NOTES